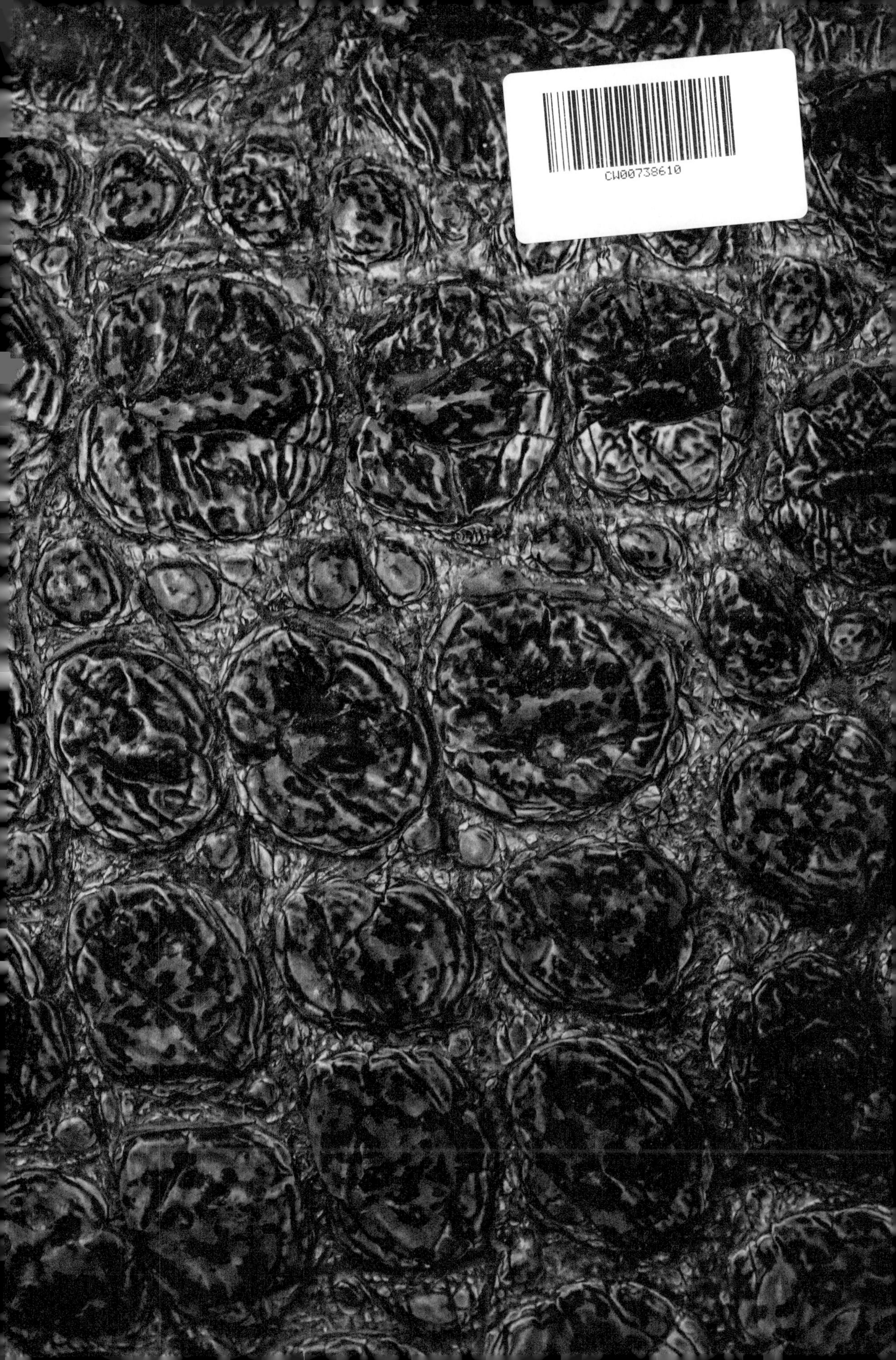
CW00738610

WHAT WE GET WRONG ABOUT CROCODILIANS

A Look at Myths, Misconceptions and Mysteries

By Jake Miller

Graphic Design by Brandon Trodick

In honor of . . .

MICHAEL J. DEE

This book is in honor of my late friend and former general curator of the Los Angeles Zoo, Michael Joseph Dee

WHAT WE GET WRONG ABOUT CROCODILIANS

ISBN: 979-8-218-03238-8 (Digital)

Front cover image by Sterling Lanier
Book Graphic Design by Brandon Trodick.

First edition 2022.

CONTENTS

ACKNOWLEDGMENTS

The past three years working on this book have been hectic to say the least. I have a lot of people to thank for helping complete this book, and acquiring the knowledge to write this book in confidence. I'd first like to say thank you to my mom and dad for supporting my passion and this journey of mine since day one. You both have always been in my corner, helping me in any way you could these last 16 years. From buying me books on these species, to planning special trips to see or interact with them, I wouldn't be where I am right now if it weren't for the both of you. I'd also like to thank the rest of my family and friends who have positively pushed me forward in my passion. You all have left a special place in my heart, and I'm eternally grateful.

Thank you to my friend Brandon Trodick for taking the time and effort to do the graphic design work for the book. You saved me a lot of time, and your input was highly appreciated. I still remember being amazed when you showed me the first draft for the book cover, and I'm impressed with the work you have done. I'd also like to thank Brandon and my other friends, Andrew, Cooper, Hunter, Jacob, Jakob, Matin, Ryan, Sam, and Sebastian for looking at parts of the book and/or giving suggestions. You all helped me tremendously.

I definitely needed help looking for the answers to some questions I had while writing this book. I'm glad to say I had some people within the crocodilian world that were there to help me out when I asked for it. I'd like to thank Brandon Sideleau, Christopher Murray, Colin Stevenson, Grahame Webb, and John Brueggen for answering my questions and/or pointing me in the direction of where I could find certain information. I am grateful to you all for taking the time to answer my much needed questions.

I'd like to also thank the late Steve Irwin for inspiring the passion I have for crocodilians. If it were not for him, I would not be on this journey of life that I am on right now. I would not know my purpose in life at the age of three years old. I am utterly grateful his enthusiasm and passion for these creatures rubbed off on me. My life is happy and full of purpose because of him, so I can not thank him enough.

Last, but not least, I would like to thank my late friend Michael J. Dee, who this book is in honor of. I met Mike at the Reptile Super Show in southern California in the early 2010's at his booth, selling his old reptile books. My parents and I started talking to Mike, talking about crocodilians and the passion for reptiles we both had. During that conversation, he told us about his experience with alligators and that he was the former general curator of the Los Angeles Zoo! From that day on, Mike gave me free books on crocodilians, which I greatly appreciated. Many of those books were used as references for this book, so in a way Mike helped me out. As a present for one of my birthdays, Mike had one of the reptile keepers shout out my name during one of the public crocodilian feedings and allowed me to interview the keeper. I definitely was lucky to have Mike be part of my life. The last time I saw Mike before his passing was at another reptile convention, and as always I got more books. As my family and I walked away saying our goodbyes, Mike pointed at me and said "I expect great things out of you." Those were the last words I ever heard him say to me. I hope you're looking down proud of me and this book Mike.

PREFACE

One of, if not the earliest memory I have is of me at three years old laying on the floor with my favorite toy, a 2 ft plastic crocodile, while I watched Steve Irwin's *The Crocodile Hunter* on my TV. I would watch him as he wrangled large Saltwater Crocodiles and I would copy him with my toy. It was at this age I knew my purpose in life was to study these animals. For the longest time I've been fascinated by crocodilians. From their powerful bite force, the caring nature for their young, their incredible and efficient white blood cells, and more, these creatures truly are one of nature's greatest survivors. Since the age of three, I have been on a journey to truly understand these creatures. Days were spent as a child watching documentaries, especially *The Crocodile Hunter*, and reading books at any chance I got. In fact, the first book I ever was able to read on my own as a young child was about the anatomy of the Nile Crocodile. Those days were the basis for my knowledge of these animals, and it only grew from there.

When learning about something over the course of a long period of time, not only are new things learned, but there is also a deeper clarity of what was previously known. An example of this occurred when I obtained what I consider the holy grail of crocodilian books up to the date of this book's publication, *Biology and Evolution of Crocodylians* by Gordon Grigg and David Kirshner. That book is the most comprehensive of all the books I have personally read on the species. What shocked me more than the level of detail that the book went on about these creatures, is the sudden realization that a couple facts that I previously believed were true, were actually false (those two subjects being in this book I should note). I was indeed shocked when I realized that fundamental facts that I thought were true since my childhood were indeed wrong, or too simplified to even just be generalizations. I even find it amazing that I see those of higher positions in places such as zoos, aquariums, and museums spouting this information, when the facts if you look into it say otherwise.

I decided to write this book because I felt that this was the one subject area where I could make my mark on crocodilian books. I had always wanted to write a book on them since I was in preschool. I even wrote a couple incomplete drafts, one on the American Alligator, and the other a comprehensive book on all the species. I came up with the idea for this book after realizing how much I had learned over all the years studying these animals, and how much has changed scientifically since I was just three years old. A book addressing what we still don't understand and get wrong about these animals seemed unique to me, and I felt like I should go for it.

I'm also writing this book as a love letter for all the years I have spent dedicating my life to better understanding these remarkable animals. This book is also a thank you to all the people that have helped me in my journey along the way. Each and every person who has encouraged me on this journey has left a mark on me and you are truly appreciated. This journey of mine is my life, and writing and completing this book is a notable chapter in it.

The book will cover a variety of subjects such as urban legends, taxonomy, biology, behavior, evolution, and more. Some of the topics will be recognizable, some are generally unknown to many, and some may be shocking. These talking points range from 5th century B.C.E. to within the last few years up to this book's date of publication. I wrote this book for anyone who is genuinely interested in these species. Whether you are casually interested in crocodilians, or have spent decades studying them, you'll get something out of this book. So let's get to it, what do we get wrong about crocodilians?

LIVING FOSSILS

It has been thought for many years that crocodilians are living fossils, unchanged since the age of the dinosaurs. However, when looking at the whole lineage of these creatures, this statement could not be further from the truth. Looking back at the many species from the superorder Crocodylomorpha, which began in the Triassic, there was a large diversity of body plans.

The first species of crocodylomorphs from the Triassic were smaller, terrestrial predators with long limbs, and there is a very slight possibility that these first animals were endothermic. Both of these characteristics differ from today's semiaquatic and ectothermic crocodilians. From these initial crocodylomorphs, they evolved into several different body plans. Many did begin to pick up the semiaquatic body plan, but others remained terrestrial and kept the longer limbs in addition to other strange features. Some had unique armor, such as *Armadillosuchus arrudi*, whose armor structure was similar to an armadillo. Some species didn't resemble modern day crocodilians at all like *Simosuchus clarki*. It had a pug-like face and a much shorter tail, looking nothing like the creature's of today. Some even evolved for an almost entirely aquatic lifestyle in the ocean like the Thallatosuchians, who had fins as well as reduced body armor to be more streamlined for swimming. Diets varied among the species too as some were carnivores, some omnivores, and some herbivores. After the K-Pg extinction 66 million years ago, much of this diversity faded, but it did not end there.

The terrestrial and 20 inch (50 cm) Terrestrisuchus gracilis *was among some of the very first crocodylomorphs during the Triassic.*

There was a large diversity of body plans within Crocodylomorpha before the K-Pg mass extinction as shown with Dakosaurus maximus *(top left),* Simosuchus clarki *(top right),* Armadillosuchus arrudai *(middle), and* Isisfordia duncani *(bottom). It is believed* Dakosaurus maximus *and* Isisfordia duncani *were both carnivorous, while* Armadillosuchus arrudai *was an omnivore, and* Simosuchus clarki *was herbivorous.*

Even the Order Crocodylia, which includes the living species, have extinct members after the K-Pg mass extinction which differed from the creatures of now. Many species were still terrestrial and the species in the genus *Boverisuchus* are particularly interesting examples. With their hoof-like foot structures, they seemed to be more terrestrial than aquatic. They also had blade-like, serrated teeth unlike the conical teeth of today's crocodilians. The only somewhat terrestrial species that remain are the Cuban Crocodile, the Freshwater Crocodile, the Cuvier's Dwarf Caiman, the Smooth-fronted Caiman, and the Dwarf Crocodile, which don't even compare to these extinct species. A few terrestrial species may have surprisingly been arboreal too, such as some of the mekosuchines. Even some of the extinct aquatic species had distinctive features. The species in the genus *Mourasuchus*, which were caimans, had unique skull morphologies as they had very broad and flat snouts. Christopher Brochu, a paleontologist and systematist of crocodylomorphs and crocodilians, described the skull of one perfectly as a "surfboard with eyeballs."

A diversity within Crocodylia after the K-Pg mass extinction still existed with terrestrial Boverisuchus magnifrons *(top), long and flat snouted* Mourasuchus pattersoni *(bottom left), and possibly arboreal* Mekosuchus inexpecatus *(bottom right) as examples.*

The reason the term living fossils has been associated with crocodilians for such a long time is a mixture of two things. First, there is no doubt that by the Jurassic there were indeed creatures that looked like today's crocodilians. However, these animals do not mean that every single crocodylomorph shared that same physical appearance, and that there was no diversity in morphologies. The second reason dates back to the 19th century. Paleontologists of the time found many incomplete and fragmented fossils that seemingly looked like those of the modern day species. Some were even classified in the same genera as living crocodiles. To quote William Buckland, an early paleontologist and theologian, "fossil reptiles of the Crocodilean family do not deviate sufficiently from living genera to require any description of peculiar and discontinued contrivances." He also reasoned that due to fish being abundant at the time of the first crocodylomorphs, they must have had thin snouts to be more hydrodynamic for hunting, like the Indian Gharial. This adds to the notion that these creatures were always in the water. However, as time went on, more species as well as more complete fossils were found, showing a greater diversity of animals.

William Buckland and other paleontologists from the past influenced the misconception of crocodilians being living fossils.

THE SNOUT RULE

A popular method people use to differentiate alligators from crocodiles is the snout rule. The rule states that if the snout of the animal is wide and U-shaped it's an alligator, and if it is thinner and V-shaped it's a crocodile. This holds true in the Everglades with both native crocodilians, the American Alligator and the American Crocodile. However, this rule is too simple to apply to the diversity of snout shapes in all living species and how snout shape changes in an individual's life.

Many exceptions exist in this rule. There are species of crocodiles with naturally broad snouts such as the Mugger Crocodile, Morelet's Crocodile, African Dwarf Crocodile, and Siamese Crocodile. There are also species of caiman, which are in the same family as alligators, that have thinner snouts, including certain subspecies of Spectacled Caiman (especially the Rio Apaporis Caiman, *Caiman crocodilus apaporiensis*) and the Smooth-fronted Caiman. To make things more complicated, snouts can change throughout an animal's life. In many crocodile species, hatchlings may not have naturally broad snouts. They would begin with a thinner V-shaped snout in their life. However, as they get older and larger (especially in terms of mass), their entire skull will begin to widen and thicken. Thus, the typical V-shape of the snout will be lost, and they will gain a broad U-shaped snout. This mainly occurs with males. With these two factors in mind, snout shape can't be a conclusive way to tell crocodiles and alligators apart.

As an Individual grows, its skull will begin to become larger and much thicker, as seen with these Saltwater Crocodiles of different sizes.

Crocodiles with broad snouts, like the American Alligator (top left), include the Dwarf Crocodile (top middle), Morelet's Crocodile (top right), Mugger Crocodile (bottom left), and Siamese Crocodile (bottom right).

Species within the family Alligatoridae which have thinner snouts, like the American Crocodile (left), include the Smooth-fronted Caiman (middle) and Spectacled Caiman (right).

However, there are still other ways to tell them apart, which are true for all extant species. When an alligator's jaws are closed, you can only see the upper teeth as the lower teeth fit into pockets in the upper jaw, but in crocodiles you can see both the upper and lower teeth. This method may not work though if the crocodilian has metabolic bone disease and sprawled teeth, but is still helpful. Crocodiles also have salt glands to tolerate saltwater on their tongues, but this is absent in alligators. All crocodilians have integumentary sense organs (ISOs) for detecting vibrations in the water on their scales, which look like black dots. However, the area these cover differs in alligators and crocodiles. In alligators they only have ISOs on their jawline, but in crocodiles they have these throughout their entire body, typically one for each scale.

Instead of head structure being due to cladistic or taxonomic reasons, it is due to the hunting lifestyle of different species. Thinner snouts are associated with less water drag when hunting for animals, like fish, for quicker attacks under water, while broader and larger snouts are associated with crushing power to tackle large and/or hard shelled prey. However, this does not mean that animals with certain jaws are specialists. Crocodilians with broader snouts still have fish as a large portion of their diet, and those with thinner snouts will still go after larger and non aquatic prey. A perfect example of this is the Tomistoma. It is a thin snouted species, also named the False Gharial due to its snout, but it will still go after larger prey such as monkeys. There has even been an eye witness account of one attacking a cow and one confirmed case of a Tomistoma attacking and eating an adult human. The only specialized species among crocodilians are the Indian Gharials, with their extremely thin snouts meant for hunting fish, but rare incidents of larger gharials eating mammals have been reported.

Broad-snouted Caimans have broad jaws equipped for crushing aquatic snails, turtles, and crustaceans.

The Tomistoma's thin snout allows it to catch aquatic prey much faster. However, it is still capable of hunting much larger prey items including humans.

Adult Indian Gharials eat almost exclusively fish due to their thin snouts. However, rare reports of them eating mammals do exist.

CROCODILE TEARS

The common phrase "crocodile tears" is used when a person is accused of fake crying or crying insincerely. Not only is this phrase used for real life situations, but it is also commonly used in political or social cartoons. The phrase is based on stories of crocodilians crying to lure their prey, as well as them crying during their meals. This mainly comes from European sources and started as early as the 13th century from Bartholomaeus Anglicus, a Franciscan monk. He wrote in an encyclopedia of natural sciences that "If the crocodile findeth a man by the brim of the water, or by the cliff, he slayeth him there if he may, and then weepeth upon him and swalloweth him at last". However, it would be due to the book *The Travels of Sir John Mandeville*, released in the 14th century, that this idea of crocodiles crying would be spread more widely. The book stated "In that contre-- ben gret plentee of cokodrilles. Theise serpentes slen men, and thei eten hem wepynge" Others spread this claim of crocodiles going forward such as "His nature is ever when hee would have his prey, to cry and sobbe like a christian body, to provoke them to come to him, and then hee snatcheth at them…" from adventurer John Sparke, and "...the crocodile, when he hath devoured a man and eaten up all but the head, will sit and weep over it as of he expressed a great portion of sorrow for his cruel feast, but it is nothing so, for when he weeps it is because his hungrie painch wants such another prey." from writer John Swan.

Crocodilians do not seem to cry for emotional reasons, such as humans, and most definitely do not cry to attract prey. However, there is a hint of truth to this myth. Not only do the tears lubricate the eyes when they dry up from basking, but it has also been observed that crocodilians will become teary eyed when eating. The specific reason as to why they "cry" when eating is up for debate, but it seems to be physiological rather than emotional. One hypothesis is that it's possible the hissing and huffs the animals make during eating forces air into the sinuses and stimulates tears. Another is the extensive jaw pressure the animals exert squeezes tears to come out. There's also the thought that the tears are always present underneath the eyes, coming out when the animal is attacking prey or simply thrashing its head. The tears may be used for a defensive purpose in this case, as the tears would protect the eye from debris. Whatever the case may be, if you see a crocodilian with a tear running down its eye, it's certainly not trying to make you its next meal.

This political cartoon depicts Ulysses S. Grant crying crocodile tears, as he weeps over how Jews are persecuted in Russia.

INTELLIGENCE LEVEL

Many people consider crocodilians as dumb brutes with no thought process. That they are mindless killing machines with no intellect. It is the author's experience that guests at zoos will even comment on how low their intelligence is when seeing them. However, these comments are extremely ignorant. Crocodilians are not only the smartest reptiles, they are also smarter than people give them credit for.

Crocodilians are the only species of reptiles to have a cerebral cortex in their brain. The cerebral cortex plays an important part in memory, and crocodilians seem to showcase a great capacity for memorization. In captive settings, crocodilians learn commands such as stop and go, and even the appropriate distance to approach a keeper. These techniques make it safer for the keeper and the animal. At many zoos, animals are assigned names and when a keeper calls a name in a group of crocodilians, the animal with that specific name will be the only one to approach the keeper. They can even pick up the routines of the keepers as well. The author will note in 2015 how a male Tomistoma was lying still in the water 10-15 minutes before the keepers came to feed it at the Los Angeles Zoo. After the normal background sounds of frogs croaking at the reptile house had been turned off, the tomistoma suddenly started swimming in circles near the feeding dock where the keepers fed him. If the author remembers correctly, after the author told this to a keeper, the keeper explained they would shut the noise off before feeding the tomistomas. If this is the case, the tomistoma had learned when it would be fed. Crocodilians can even learn target training for food. The individual animal will either tap its snout or strike at the target, and then the animal will receive food. Some keepers have even tried to use whistles to tell the animal they've done a correct response. In addition, many zoos have trained the crocodilians to be desensitized so that medical checks can occur without restraining the animal.

In terms of hunting, crocodilians have been reported to pick up habits of their prey. They will stalk a prey item and pick up where it likes to drink, eat, and rest in order to understand its habits. Also, while there is some debate if this is intentional or not, it has been observed Mugger Crocodiles and American Alligators will place sticks on their snouts for birds to swoop down and grab them. The sticks appear to be bait for the birds so the crocodilians can eat them more easily. At least for the American Alligator, this seems to occur during nesting season for the birds, as the sticks are a required item for them to build their nests. If this is intentional, this is the first recorded occurrence of tool use in reptiles. In addition to these hunting strategies, it has been suggested Cuban Crocodiles exhibit pack hunting behaviors, as some in zoos show examples of coordinated attacks. Some species have been documented in the wild to congregate in a line or half circle to trap incoming fish from a canal or river, allowing all crocodilians involved to get a meal as well.

Crocodilians also exhibit excellent homing capabilities. It has been documented several times that when mature crocodilians are removed from their original "homes" and relocated to a different location miles away, they will return to the location where they were captured. A study in Queensland, Australia showed how one male Saltwater Crocodile with a satellite transmitter had a particularly incredible homing ability. After he had been captured from the west side of the Cape York Peninsula and relocated to the east side, he spent 108 days at this release site. Then, he swam around the coast for over 20 days and returned to the exact same river he was captured. The total distance the crocodile traveled was 255 miles (410 km). There are certainly more to crocodilians than meets the eye.

Keepers, like these at the Naples Zoo, will individually call the American Alligators up to them for feeding demonstrations.

The feeding dock of the Los Angeles Zoo where the author saw a male Tomistoma swim around the dock anticipating the keeper to come. The picture above was taken 4 years after the author's observation and shows a female, but serves as a visual for what was seen in 2015. It should be noted that the author only saw this behavior once and that by at least 2018 they no longer shut off the frog croaking background sound effect. Therefore, the author never saw the behavior exhibited again.

Cuban Crocodiles have claims of hunting in coordinated or pack-like behavior in captive settings.

Many crocodilians, including the Saltwater Crocodile shown above, have been documented traveling long distances to return to locations where they were originally captured after relocation.

ENORMOUS CROCODILIANS

This is a regularly occurring problem, specifically with many books, where the length of a species is exaggerated to some degree, and the lengths stated are many times not even verified. Sources often claim that many crocodilians can get up to 20 feet (6.1 m) or more in length, and that this is a somewhat normal maximum. However, reality shows the chance of seeing a 20 ft crocodilian, or one bigger, is extremely rare. Most individuals, like the Saltwater and Nile crocodile, max out at around 16-18 ft (4.9-5.5 m) in length, and it's an incredible sight to see those individuals as those of that size are scarce. People many times don't even realize how amazing it is to see just a 15 ft (4.6 m) crocodile and appreciate how rare it is. The average size for large crocodilians is around 12-14 ft (3.7-4.3 m) in length and is what's common. There has been this long assumption that these "Monster Crocodiles" are commonplace, but few of these animals really exist anymore. The reasons these reports exist are mainly due to two reasons, unverified stories, and remains of dead individuals.

Many times, these claims come from eye witness accounts or stories, not from verified measurements. For example, the 23 foot (7 m) long measurement often associated with the Saltwater Crocodile comes from a person's observation in the Bhitarkanika National Park in Odisha, India. An actual measurement never occurred. The problem with this is people constantly have a hard time telling how big a crocodilian is by looking at it. In addition, eye witnesses tend to overestimate the size of these animals, many times claiming that they are 20 ft or larger. These also extend to tall tales of unconfirmed cases of extremely large animals for many species. Three popular examples are Gustave, Krys, and an extremely large American Alligator from the 1800's. Gustave is a famous 20 ft Nile Crocodile from Lake Tanganyika in Burundi that supposedly has killed 300 people. Krys the crocodile is a legendary 28 ft (8.6 m) Saltwater Crocodile that was killed by a hunter in 1957 in Australia. The American Alligator story is based on a hunter in the 1800's who killed an alligator that was 19 feet 2 inches (5.8m).

The other method is based on remains of deceased crocodilians. Many times there is no corpse for scientists to measure. Instead, what is mainly left over are the skulls of the animals. There has been a general assumption that you can find the length of a crocodile by simply multiplying the head length (tip of the snout to the end of the cranial platform) about seven times to find the whole length. However, the issue is that not only are there differences between species (especially longirostrine, or long and thin snouted crocodilians, as their heads make up more of their total body length), but there are also different ratios of different sized individuals of the same species. It seems the range for the head length to total body length ratio could be anywhere from 1:5 to 1:9 depending on the species and length of the individual, but even this isn't definite. This method only produces estimates, not precise lengths, but the method is still helpful. For example, the skull of a Saltwater Crocodile that had claims of being 33 ft (10.1 m) in length was preserved and later examined. The skull was just under 28 inches (71 cm) long. Even if the head length to total body length of this animal was 1:9, this would only mean the crocodile was around 21 ft (6.4 m) at most. Not the enormous 33 ft claimed. Another way to measure is skins. At least in the case of a deceased Saltwater Crocodile found in Papua New Guinea, only the head and skin remained and it was found to be 20 ft long. However, the skin had dried for several days and it is likely that the skin had shrunk. Therefore, it's possible for the crocodile to be larger than what was measured

The species that seem to be known for 20 ft+ status are spread out amongst all the extant crocodilian families. The species include the American Alligator, Black Caiman, American Crocodile, Cuban Crocodile, Orinoco Crocodile, Nile Crocodile, Saltwater Crocodile, Tomistoma, and Indian Gharial. The American Alligator claim comes from historical observations of possibly 20 ft long animals during the 18th century. The Black Caiman claim is from hunters and old literature. The American Crocodile claim is based on historical claims in old literature and hunters. The Cuban Crocodile claim is associated with large fossils, mainly skulls, being found. They indicate that during the Pleistocene, the Cuban Crocodile may have reached lengths of 20 ft or even longer. The animals of now rarely exceed 10 ft (3 m). The Orinoco Crocodile is an interesting case, as the claim is largely due to the reports made from well respected naturalist Alexander von Humboldt and botanist Aimé Bonpland. The animal recorded was 22 feet, 3 inches (6.8 m long), and was measured by Bonpland and later reported by Humboldt in 1800. The problem, however, lies with the possible mistranslation of the book this claim comes from. The Nile Crocodile claim is based on stories of hunters, folklore, as well as skulls of deceased individuals. The Saltwater Crocodile is a combination of deceased individuals, live specimens, and tales of hunters. The skulls of multiple crocodiles and skin have been found helping to validate this claim. In addition, a 20 ft long Salty was found and caught alive in the Philippines by the name of Lolong in 2011. It was the largest crocodile to ever be caught alive, and confirms this maximum in this species. Thus, the Saltwater Crocodile is the only species with a confirmed length of 20 ft. The Tomistoma's claim is based on giant skulls (the largest crocodilian skull belongs to the tomistma at 33 inches, or 84 cm) and supposedly historical claims. The Indian Gharial claim is based on stories from hunters, as well as observations and potential historical estimates. Many experts believe in the possibility of these monster crocs once living in the wild more frequently, but due to hunting, especially by the time of World War two, these animals died and their genetics went with them.

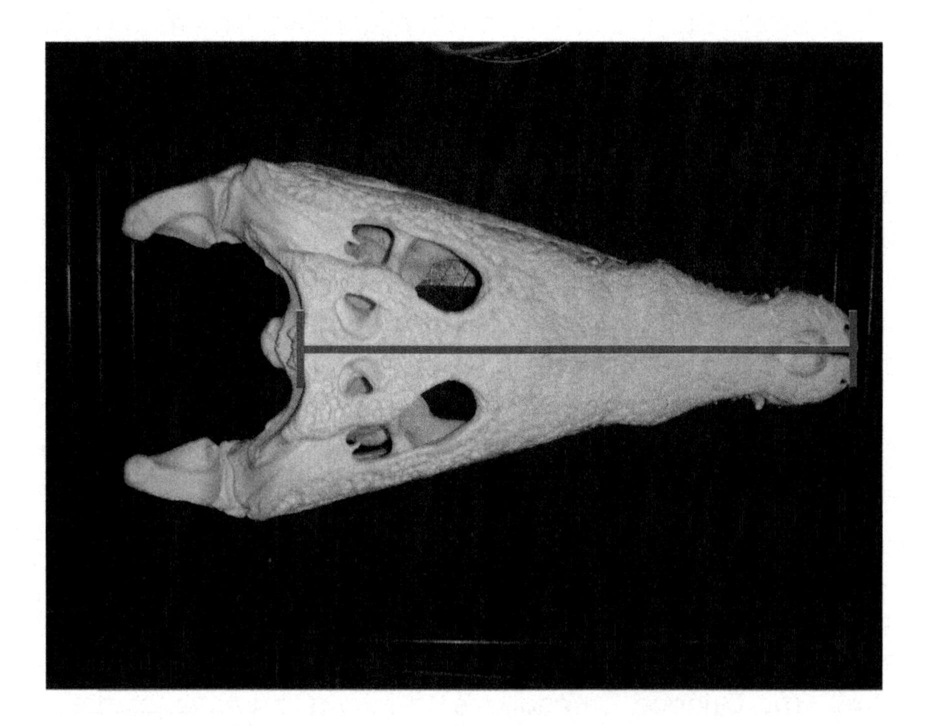

The head length to total body length ratio is based on the measurement of the tip of the snout to the end of the cranial platform, as indicated with this crocodile skull.

Species	Average Length For Males	Realistic Maximums	Enormous Examples
American Alligator 	12-13 feet (3.7-4 meters)	14-15 feet (4.3-4.6 meters)	Quaker, naturalist William Bartram during his time in Florida in the 18th century reported seeing 20 ft (6.1 m) long animals
Black Caiman 	12-13 feet (3.7-4 meters)	14-16 feet (4.3-4.9 meters)	Hunters from Bolivia report animals as long as 23 ft (7 m).
American Crocodile 	12-14 feet (3.7-4.3 meters)	15-16 feet (4.6-4.9 meters)	Biologist Miguel Álvarez del Toro wrote that animals with lengths of 20.5 ft (6.25 m) once existed, but are no longer common.
Cuban Crocodile 	8-9 feet (2.4-2.7 meters)	10-11 feet (3-3.4 meters)	Skulls found from the Pleistocene suggest animals with lengths of 20 ft (6.1 m) or more once existed.
Orinoco Crocodile 	12-14 feet (3.7-4.3 meters)	15-16 feet (4.6-4.9 meters)	Alexander von Humboldt and Aimé Bonpland supposedly reported in 1800 that a 22 foot, 3 inch (6.3 m) individual existed.

Species	Average Length For Males	Realistic Maximums	Enormous Examples
Nile Crocodile 	12-14 feet (3.7-4.3 meters)	15-18 feet (4.6-5.5 meters)	English explorer and scientific writer Mary H. Kingsley reported in 1897 the largest Nile Crocodile she ever measured was 22 feet and 3 inches (6.3 m).
Saltwater Crocodile 	12-14 feet (3.7-4.3 meters)	15-18 feet (4.6-5.5 meters)	A 33 ft (10.1 m) Saltwater Crocodile was supposedly shot in Bay of Bengal in 1840.
Tomistoma 	12-14 feet (3.7-4.3 meters)	15-17 feet (4.6-5.2 meters)	Herpetologists Romulus and Nik Whitaker wrote in a study they were “quite certain” Tomistomas could reach lengths of 20 ft (6.1 m) and above based on skulls.
Indian Gharial 	13-14 feet (4-4.3 meters)	15-18 feet (4.6-5.5 meters)	Captain J. Johansen claimed to have seen Indian Gharials as long as 22 to 30 ft (6.7-9.1 m) from the late 19th to early 20th century.

Lolong was a 20.2 ft (6.2 m) Saltwater Crocodile caught in the Philippines and was the largest crocodile to ever be caught alive. He helps confirm the Saltwater Crocodile can reach lengths of 20 ft.

MONSTERS CLOSER UP

GUSTAVE

Gustave is a Nile Crocodile from Lake Tanganyika in Burundi suspected to be 20 ft long, but some say he's 30 to 40 ft (9.1-12.2 m) in length. His name comes from French environmentalist Patrice Faye, who worked in Burundi and had an interest in the crocodile. Gustave supposedly has a kill count of 300 people, along with a claim of eating an entire hippo. He is said to have a technique of splashing water at fishermen with his tail, making them fall off the canoes or draft boats they were standing on to make a meal of them. It's easy to see why Gustave has a mythical status to him, but there are many problems surrounding the story of this crocodile. Firstly, the 300 number seems to be exaggerated as Patrice Faye has said Gustave has only killed 60 people at most, maybe even less. Secondly, even if 300 attacks did occur, they most likely involved different crocodiles. Brandon Sideleau, an expert in human-crocodile conflict, told the author multiple photos of "Gustave" seem to be of different individuals. Lastly, there is no confirmed evidence of Gustave being 20 ft, and the 30 to 40 ft observations seem too absurd to be plausible. As astounding as Gustave's claims are, there is no confirmation for any of these assertions.

KRYS

Krys "The Savannah King" is a legendary, 28 ft (8.5 m) long Saltwater Crocodile that was killed by hunter Kris Pawlowski, and measured by her husband, Ron Pawlowski. It was shot in 1957 at the Norman River in Queensland, Australia and was so large that the body of the croc could not be moved. Supposedly a picture of this behemoth was taken, but was lost in the Brisbane Floods of 1974. Whether Krys did indeed exist is up to one's belief in the story. Other than the supposed picture, nothing was ever officially recorded to verify the story. However, Grahame Webb, a well respected crocodile expert who was deeply involved in the early conservation of the Saltwater Crocodile, believes the story. He spoke with Ron Pawlowski about the story and says "I spent three days talking with Ron and everything else he told me about crocodiles turned out to be very precise indeed. I can't imagine him fabricating something like this." Grahame Webb also told the author how Ron described the eyes of Krys as huge, like an apple. While Krys can't be considered the largest recorded crocodile due to a lack of evidence, it is still an interesting story if true.

MCILHENNY'S ALLIGATOR

In 1890, 17 year old Edward Avery McIlhenny claimed to have measured a 19 foot, 2 inch (5.8 m) long American Alligator in Louisiana. While hunting mallards, he came across a very large alligator in the water and shot it in the head. McIlhenny and some friends tried to retrieve the carcass of the gator, but it was too large to drag through the marsh. McIlhenny then measured the alligator's length with the barrel of his shotgun, which was 30 inches (76.2 cm), and measured it three different times. The alligator's length was 19 feet, 2 inches. If this is true, it would be the largest alligator ever measured, but was he telling the truth? On one hand, McIlhenny was a well educated man on alligators and even wrote a respected book titled *The Alligator's Life History* in 1935. On the other hand, McIlhenny was well known for telling tall tales such as him being responsible for the introduction of Nutria to Louisiana. Shane Bernard, the historian for McIlhenny's tabasco company, the McIlhenny Company, even stated "I think he saw himself as an entertainer when relating his personal history. He took liberties in a good-natured way." The validity of this claim seems to be up in the air as of now.

TROCHILUS/PLOVER AND OTHER SYMBIOTIC RELATIONSHIPS

Something famously associated with the Nile Crocodile is that they have a supposed symbiotic relationship with plovers, where the plovers clean the teeth of the crocodiles. This first came from the Greek philosopher Herodotus in the 5th century B.C.E and the bird described was called the Trochilus, which is often associated with the Egyptian Plover and/or the Spur-winged Plover. Allegedly, the crocodile will open its jaws to allow the plover to enter, and the plover will then clean the crocodile's jaws and teeth of leeches and old food. The crocodile ends up with clean jaws and the plover gets a meal out of it. Many people from the 16th century and after have claimed validity for this relationship including, but not limited to, traveler and writer Joannes Leo Africanus, naturalist Geoffroy St.-Hilaire, director of the Humburg Zoological Gardens Alfred Edmund Brehm, ornithologist Richard Meinertzhagen, and zoologist Hugh Cott. In the case of Hugh Cott's claim in a 1961 research paper, he reported the Egyptian Plover and Spur-winged Plover were the birds mainly seen removing skin parasites, as well as aquatic snails, leeches, and food leftovers from the jaws of crocodiles. He also stated Common Sandpipers could be seen doing the same thing.

An illustration of the Trochilus and Nile Crocodile relationship described originally by Herodotus.

Although talked about many times from different sources, this behavior has never been actually confirmed. All photographic and video evidence shown publicly has been proven to be digitally edited, and while there have been a few eyewitness accounts within the last 100 years from some safari people in Africa, these have not been verified.

Naturalist Charles Albert Walter Guggisberg did state that "I have been told that a photograph showing Egyptian plovers in a crocodile's mouth was published in a German book, but my informant could not remember either the author or the title." So this particular claim can not be seen as 100% valid. Considering all the documentaries centered on the Nile Crocodile within the last 50 years too, there is no doubt this behavior should have been filmed by now. It's worth mentioning as well that Herodotus is known for exaggerated or false claims such as lion cubs clawing in their mother's womb until their birth, hippos having "snub" noses, and crocodiles having fixed lower jaws. Also, it wouldn't make sense for a relationship like this to exist. Crocodiles go through hundreds to thousands of teeth throughout their lifetime, so a problem with a tooth should not be an issue for an individual. Also, there is some thought that the jaw gapping crocodilians do is to dry out their jaws and discourage leeches, so this isn't to simply allow birds to enter. Furthermore, birds have been seen to hunt insects around basking crocodiles, and the crocodiles don't seem too interested in them. Therefore, it's possible that this is not a mutualistic relationship, but just birds being opportunistic. At least as of now, this symbiotic relationship can not be seen as fact.

Images such as this are digital reconstructions. No real photographs of this relationship exist or have been confirmed as of the date of this book's publication.

There are a few other symbiotic relationships that are not too often discussed in relation to crocodilians. One includes the crocodilians of Costa Rica and some species of butterflies, bees, and moths. It has been observed many times that butterflies, bees, and moths will hang out near the heads of crocodilians and drink their tears. While this doesn't harm or benefit the crocodilian, the tears seem to have a nutritional value that the insects value, possibly salt and proteins. Another is the stomach parasites of crocodilians aiding them in highly polluted environments. One study found that the intestinal trematodes of American Alligators accumulated enough of the heavy metals inside the animals, so that the metals weren't hariming the alligators. In terms of other crocodilians being cleaned by other animals, it has also been claimed that cleaner fish will clean the teeth of American Crocodiles, American Alligators, and possibly other species in the wild. In additon, it's been claimed sandpipers clean the teeth of Saltwater Crocodiles in the wild, but this hasn't been confirmed.

Butterflies are seen drinking the tears of this Morelet's Crocodile. The tears seem to have a nutritional value that the butterflies value.

A photo online shows fish inside the jaws of a Dwarf Crocodile at the Minnesota Zoo, with a description that the fish are cleaning the crocodile's teeth. "West African Dwarf Crocodile, Osteolaemus tetraspis getting the inside of his mouth cleaned by cleaner fish which removes and eats parasites and other materials."

RUNNING SPEEDS

It has long been stated that crocodilians are extremely fast on land. Claims such as them running anywhere from 20-50 mph (32.2-80.5 km/h) for short distances, and them even being able to race with horses have been said. There is even the famous survival tip that to outrun an alligator or crocodile, one must run in a zigzag formation. However, if you were to really look at these animals, you would see how ridiculous those statements are. In reality, a crocodilian can only run 10 mph (16.1 km/h) at most in short bursts.

It is quite obvious when looking at extant crocodilians that they are made more for an aquatic lifestyle than a terrestrial one. They have relatively short legs and they do not need long powerful legs to do their job as predators. If they are moving towards prey, they most likely wil either either strike from the water's edge, swim after it, or jump vertically into the air from the water. While crocodilians will occasionally run after prey after a strike at the water's edge, this occurs only briefly. They won't pursue their prey in a high speed chase over long distances. It should be noted that in captivity, if enticed by the keeper, the crocodilian may continue following the keeper feeding them. This is not as if it's chasing the keeper though, just following the food. It seems that the top speed of crocodilians is anywhere from 5-10 mph (8-16.1 km/h), and they don't run at these speeds often. The vast majority of the time they're taking their time moving on land. Crocodilians in general only move fast on land when avoiding danger or wanting to get back in the water. However, they will briefly come out of the water to pursue prey, as stated previously, and adult males and females will shortly chase away threats to their nest.

It seems that the faster crocodilians are both the smaller species and smaller individuals, as an increase in their mass seems to slow them down. Another interesting discovery is that, generally, the limbs of crocodiles are slightly longer than alligators and caimans, making alligators and caimans less equipped for a terrestrial lifestyle. This may be the reason why alligators and caimans can't gallop like crocodiles can. Interestingly, one study has stated even with the lack of this gait, alligators and caimans run at the same speeds as crocodiles.

The only species known to be somewhat fast on land are the Freshwater Crocodile and the Cuban Crocodile. The Freshwater Crocodile is well known for its galloping and seems to have the fastest recorded speed of any crocodilian, at just over 10 mph. The Cuban Crocodile has evolved to be somewhat terrestrial with longer limbs, as its species used to eat the now extinct Ground Sloth. This species is dangerous as mature individuals still run at fast speeds, and are known to chase zookeepers. A true exception to other crocodilians. One keeper at GatorLand claimed the Cuban's can run at 17 mph (27.4 km/h) in short bursts to the author, but this is unconfirmed (looking back the keeper may have meant 17 km/h, or 10.5 mph, which is plausible). Still, a healthy adult human can outrun any crocodilian if they run in a straight line. In general, just stay 30 feet (9.1 m) from the water's edge or the animal, and a person can remain safe.

Most crocodilians run so they can escape from danger and enter into the water, like this Nile Crocodile.

The Freshwater Crocodile is the fastest recorded crocodilian at 10 miles per hour.

ALLIGATORS LIVING IN NEW YORK SEWERS

One of the most popular legends regarding these creatures is that they inhabit the sewers of New York. Supposedly there are not just a few alligators, but an entire colony living beneath the residents of New York. Some are albino, and some may be mutated. This urban legend of alligators living in sewers in general dates back to the early 20th century. One example includes a story from the New York Times in 1907, when an 18 inch (46 cm) baby alligator was found by a New Jersey sewer worker. Another involved a three foot (1 m) dead crocodile, which was originally reported as an alligator, being found by a couple of boys in New York in 1932. Except this time the boys claimed the Bronx River was infested with them. In addition, there were supposedly suggestions that alligators be used to help clear city sewer pipes. However, what truly gave popularity to this legend, was when an alligator was pulled out of a manhole in Harlem.

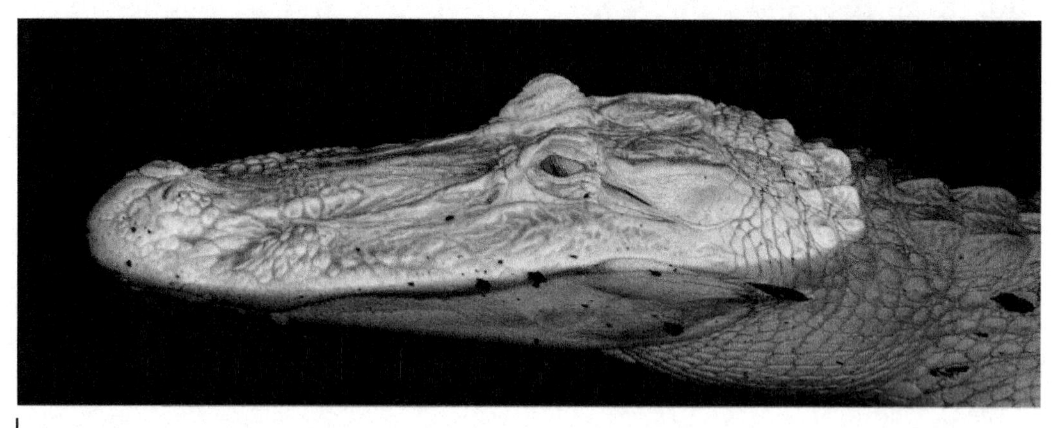

There were many rumors that the alligators living in the New York sewers were albino, but there is no real evidence for this claim.

The most famous incident that blew up this urban legend happened in 1935, when Salvatore Condoluci and his friends were shoveling snow into a manhole. They saw something moving in the sewers and decided to pull it out. It turned out to be a seven to eight foot (2.1-2.4 m), 125 pound (56.7 kg) American Alligator. The alligator was supposedly weak, but tried to bite one of the boys. After the attempted attack, the boys immediately

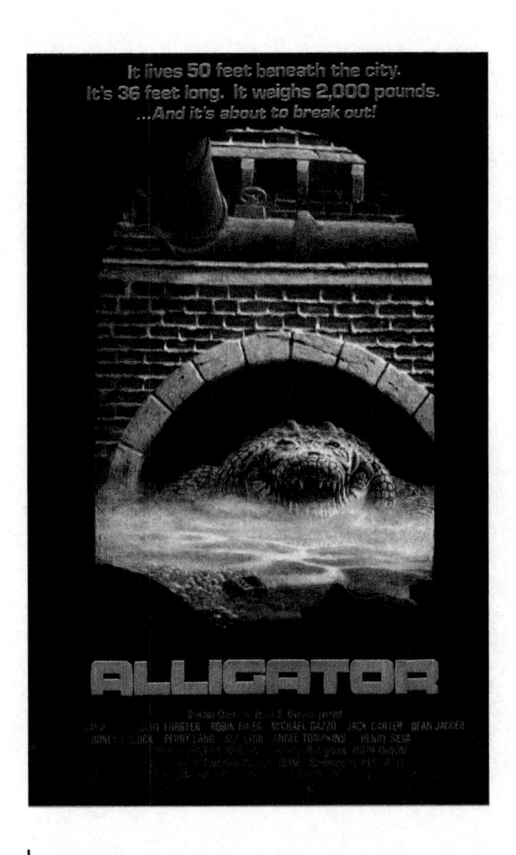

Alligators in sewers have long been part of American pop culture, as shown with this poster of the 1980 movie Alligator. *The movie is about a hatchling alligator who is flushed down the toilet and mutates into a giant alligator in the sewers of Chicago.*

beat the alligator to death with their shovels. Soon after, rumors of large alligator colonies in the sewers began to surface, which were started by Teddy May, the superintendent of sewers. Teddy's claims come from the book *The World Beneath the City* by Robert Daley, where he explains how he discovered a colony of alligators by himself in the New York sewers. Many of the alligators, however, didn't survive long based on his claims. Several factors lead to their demise such as some eating rat poison, some drowning in overflowing sewers, many being forced to leave the sewers and swim out into the sea by sewer workers, and some being shot by rifles as a pass time for workers. Ever since the Harlem incident, Teddy May's claims, and a few more alligators being found in New York, the myth of alligators living in the sewers has stayed popular in American folklore.

The question that comes to mind when reading about all these findings, is where exactly did all these alligators come from? No crocodilians are native to the north east of the United States, so they must have been brought up there, or more specifically, released from captivity. As early as the late 19th century, it was not uncommon for people to buy baby alligators as pets. Ads of live baby gators were common in newspapers, and some pet shops even sold the animals. Many times the hatchlings came from businesses in the south east of the United States. Once the owners realized the animal doesn't stay 10 inches (25 cm) and cute forever, they would eventually discard the animal. Rumors and speculations suggest people would either dump them in a public waterway, flush them down the toilet, or lift up a manhole and drop them in the sewers. Captive animals being released are not uncommon, even in other states. Two famous examples are Reggie and Chance the Snapper. Reggie was an American Alligator released into Lake Machado in Los Angeles, California in 2005. He lived in the lake for two years till his capture by Los Angeles Zoo staff, which is the zoo he now resides in. Chance the Snapper was an American Alligator found in Humboldt Park in Chicago, Illinois during 2019 and was soon captured by alligator trapper Frank Robb.

Hatchling alligators were commonly sold as pets from the late 19th century to the mid 20th century in the USA. These pet gators being released is the most common reason for them showing up outside of their native range.

Reggie the American Alligator was found in Lake Machado in Los Angeles, California in the mid 2000's. He currently lives at the Los Angeles Zoo.

So is it possible for multiple alligators to have been found in New York sewers or New York in general? The stories above do indeed prove that. Even into the 21st century, alligators and other crocodilians have been found in New York. In 2001 a Spectacled Caiman was found in Central Park, in 2010 an alligator was hiding underneath a car in Queens, and another two were found in upstate New York in 2017, just to name a few cases. However, there is barely any evidence to conclude that these animals truly live an entire lifespan in these conditions. Also, there is no confirmed evidence they lived in colonies, were albino, or even mutated. All these particular claims come from either hearsay or anecdotal evidence. Bottomline, while there is some truth and history to this urban legend, you most likely won't be seeing an alligator anytime soon in the Big Apple.

CURRENT TAXONOMY

Since the late 20th century, when the Yacare Caiman and the Philippine Crocodile were generally accepted as distinct species, the typical number of living crocodilians has been 23. However, research done in the 21st century, mainly in the 2010's, has concluded that there may be many more legitimate species. This is mostly due to the realization of many subspecies being in fact their own separate species. This was mainly found through genetic analysis, but some do have noticeable morphological differences.

New species that have been introduced/proposed with a lot of recognition are the West African Crocodile (previously a sub species of Nile Crocodile, *Crocodylus niloticus*), Congo Dwarf Crocodile and West African Dwarf Crocodile (previously subspecies of the now Central African Dwarf Crocodile, *Osteolaemus tetraspis*), Central African Slender-snouted Crocodile (previously thought to be the now West African Slender-snouted Crocodile, *Mecistops cataphractus*) , and the Hall's New Guinea Crocodile (previously thought to be the New Guinea Crocodile, *Crocodylus novaeguineae*).

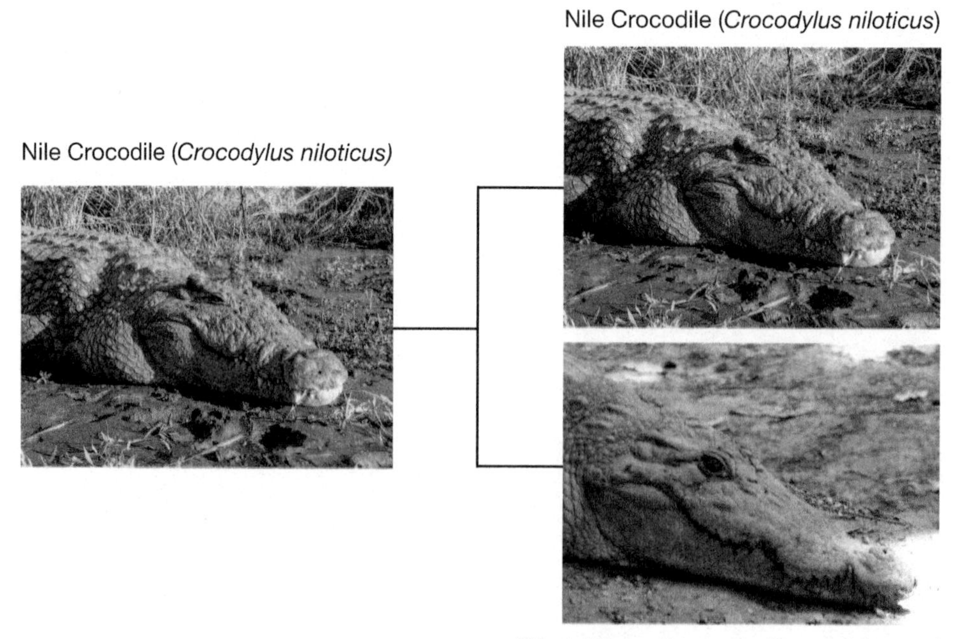

Nile Crocodile (*Crocodylus niloticus*)

Nile Crocodile (*Crocodylus niloticus*)

West African Crocodile (*Crocodylus suchus*)

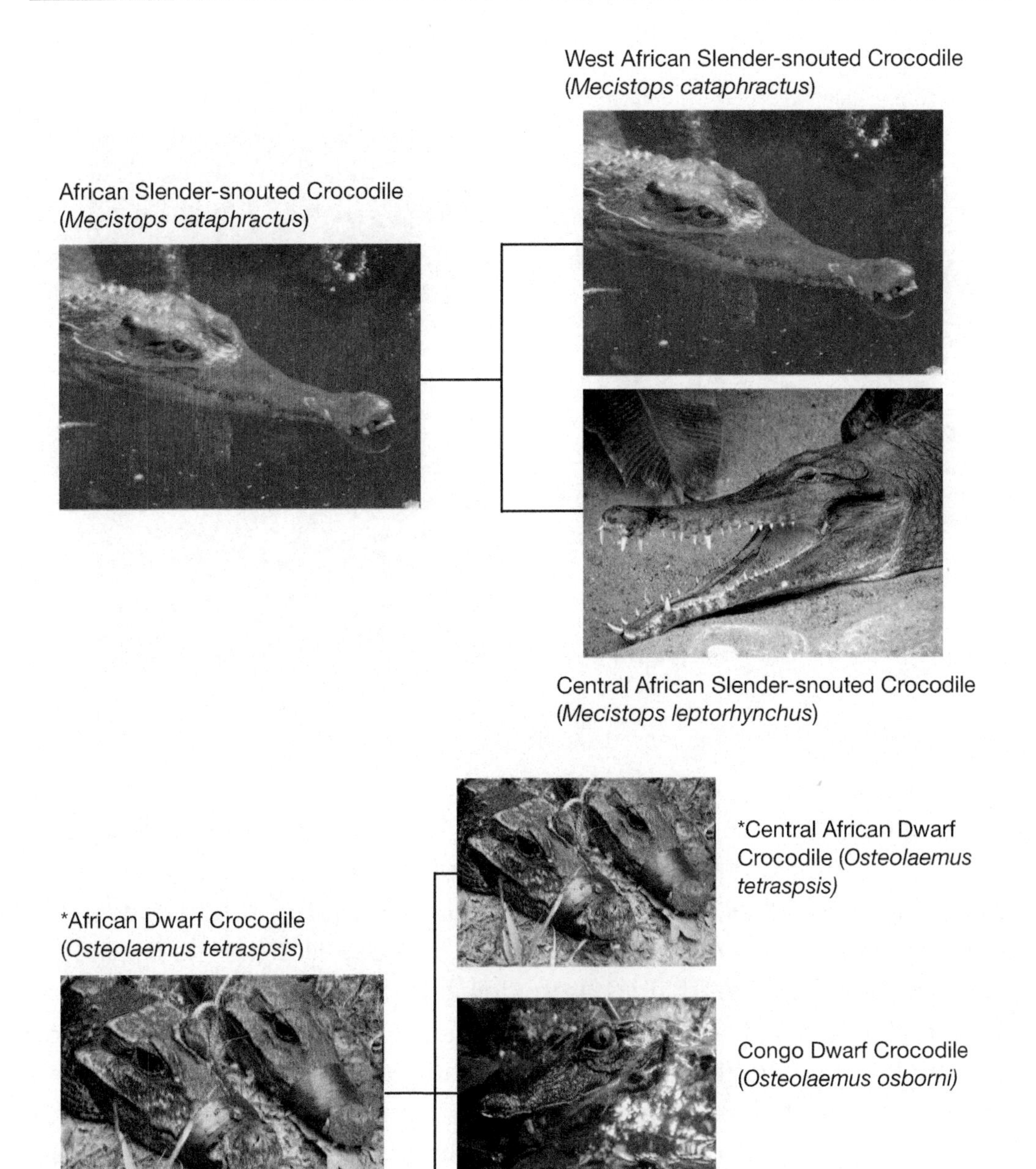

*The orange coloration is most likely due to acidic bleaching from the water the crocodile was found in.

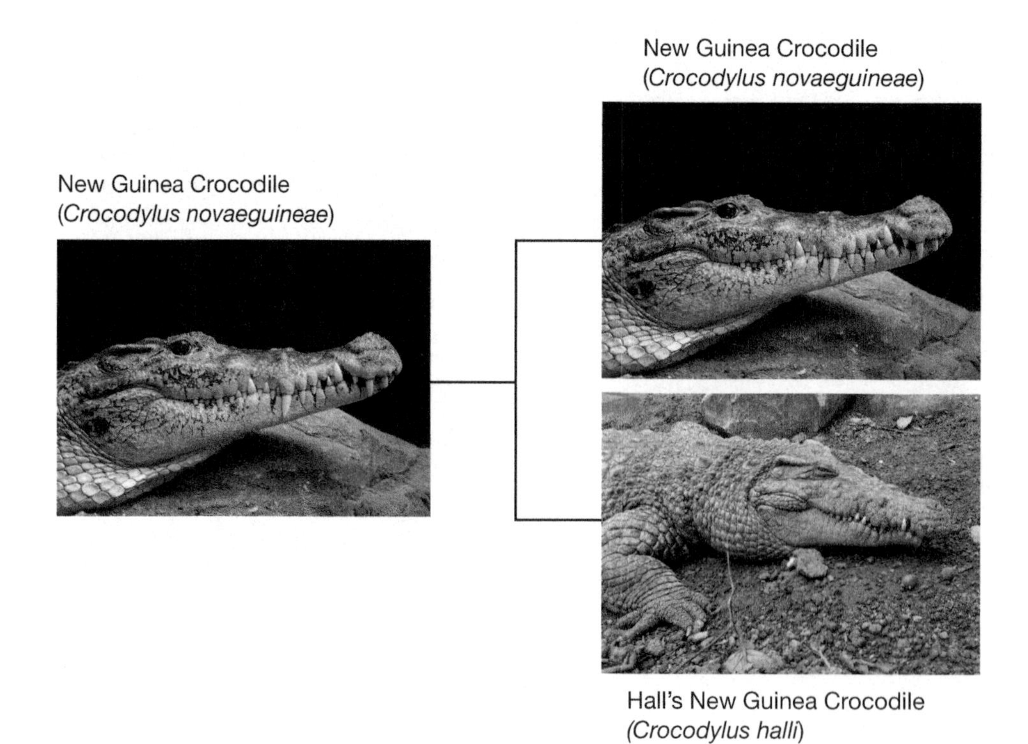

Along with the question of how many species there are, there are also arguments of whether the Tomistoma is to be considered a crocodile (part of the family Crocodylidae), or a gharial (part of the family Gavialidae). Overall morphological, evolutionary, and dietary evidence has concluded that the Tomistoma is more closely related to crocodiles than to the Indian Gharials. Studies have found that the tail and jaw musculature is different between the two, the ontogenetic trajectories of their skulls differ, differences in their skull structures exist, and both are cared for differently in terms of diet at zoos. However, molecular data, immunological evidence, and some slight morphological similarities show that the Tomisitoma is more closely related to Indian Gharials than crocodiles. There are similarities in their DNA sequences, they have comparable immune activity, there are some similarities in their skull structures, and both are the same in terms of how their scale colorations change in response to different colored environments. Thus, the Tomistoma would be placed in the family Gavialidae based on this evidence.

To add more fire to this debate, the fossil record and the molecular data have conflicting conclusions on when the genus *Tomistoma* and genus *Gavialis* diverged. Through the use of the fossil record, the Tomistoma is in the family Crocodylidae, and the *Gavialis* lineage is old, diverging during the Mesozoic, specifically the late Cretaceous. Yet if you look at the molecular evidence, not only is the Tomistoma in Gavialidae, the *Gavialis* lineage is much younger. Through these methods, the *Gavialis* lineage diverged sometime during the Cenozoic, and the last common ancestor between the Tomistoma and Indian Gharial was 31-16 million years ago. It's also possible that the slender snouted species known as the thoracosaurus, who lived during the late Cretaceous, may not be part of the *Gavialis* lineage. This would mean that *Gavialis* would not have a lineage dating as far back as the late Cretaceous, making the molecular timeline more plausible. It is easy to see why this is an extremely complex topic.

There has been much debate from the last several decades if the Tomistoma (top) should be placed in the family Crocodylidae or in the family Gavialidae with the Indian Gharial (bottom). This debate of morphological vs molecular evidence is an interesting example of how hard it is to classify life in relation to other organisms.

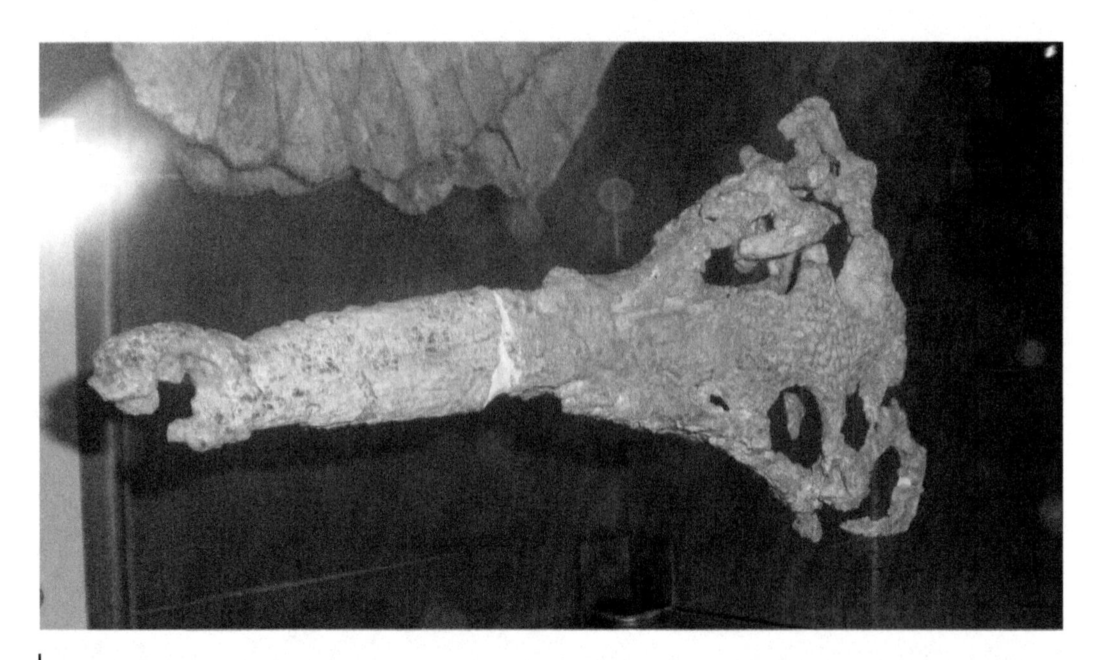

Thoracosaurs (skull of one shown above) are extinct species that have their own taxonomic problems. Some consider them as part of the Gavialis *lineage, while some do not. Their placement is important, as it helps with the current taxonomic problems surrounding the Tomistoma and Indian Gharial.*

Although the number of species and the exact taxonomy of the Tomistoma is still in debate, currently the most reliable and official international source comes from The IUCN-SSC Crocodile Specialist Group (CSG). As of now, they recognize 24 species of extant crocodilians, the new species being the West African Crocodile, but state that there is strong evidence for additional species. They also state that while there is much debate about the Tomistoma, they do recognize the species as being in Gavialidae. It should be noted, however, that the IUCN Red List lists the Tomistoma as being in Crocodylidae, but the author will regard the CSG as the definitive source. Although this is the current status of the taxonomy for extant crocodilians, it is almost certain that this will change in the future. More species level divisions have been discussed (but are less recognized) involving, but not limited to, the Yacare Caiman, Spectacled Caiman, Broad-snouted Caiman, and Tomistoma. There's even the probability of adding another Dwarf Crocodile species and the slightly possible recognition of *Crocodylus raninus* (a possible species in Borneo thought to have originally been the Saltwater Crocodile). It is very likely within the next decade we will have 30 or more crocodilian species recognized.

There is discussion of making the recently rediscovered Rio Apaporis Caiman, a subspecies of the Spectacled Caiman, its own species. It has a unique slender jaw compared to most other caimans, but genetic evidence seems to imply it's not a seperate species.

TRUE USE OF GASTROLITHS

For a lengthy period of time, it was thought that the gastroliths (stones or other hard objects with no caloric value) ingested by crocodilians were for aiding them in digestion, grinding up whatever was left to digest. An example for this reasoning came from an experiment at the Yale Peabody Museum with a caiman during the 1960's. 36 hours after the caiman ate a mouse injected with radio-opaque material, an X-ray showed that the gastroliths started to grind like "rocks in a cement machine" until the mouse was visibly unrecognizable. However, even with an example such as this, this notion is being slowly dismissed. A major reason being due to how strong their stomach acid is. Why would an animal with such an effective digestive system (which is known to have one of, if not the strongest stomach acid of any animal) need help from stones? One suggestion has been that due to crocodilians needing higher temperatures to digest food properly, if they are in a low temperature environment the stones can still break down the food. However, the stones alone would still not be

Gastroliths, such as stones like these, are common in all crocodilians. Larger individuals seem to intake these more often than juveniles for unknown reasons.

It was previously believed that crocodilians ate gastroliths to aid in digestion. This notion has been facing criticism though.

enough to fully break down the food inside their stomachs, such as the bones of the mouse for example. Other theories have been discussed ranging from buoyancy, stability, and increasing lung volume.

The first theory suggests the gastroliths help crocodilians with buoyancy when in the water. The stones, once digested, would help weigh the animal down while underwater. Research has found that in order for this idea to work, the crocodilian would need to ingest stones that are equivalent to at least 6% of its body mass to affect buoyancy. However, it seems crocodilians only take in stones that make up less than 2% of their body mass. Therefore, this can't be the reason they ingest gastroliths.

The second theory implies the gastroliths would help with stability in water. It has been noted that crocodilians are top heavy animals, and that especially younger crocodilians have a hard time stabilizing themselves in water. Therefore, it would be reasonable to think the gastroliths correct this. The gastroliths are also believed to help hold the HOTA posture (head oblique, tail arched), which is used when feeding and bellowing in the water. The gastroliths in this situation would keep the lower part of the belly anchored while the rest of the body is above water. However, there is some descent from this explanation. Crocodilians are able to change the position of their lungs, which allows for a change in their position in the water. Thus, gastroliths would not be needed for stabilization in this context. Also, the HOTA theory has been put down, as the stone amounts crocodilians use would not be enough to hold the position. It looks like stability is another questionable explanation.

The third theory is that gastroliths increase the lung volume of crocodilians. In this scenario, they would enable more air to enter the lungs, thus allowing for longer dives. It was found through a few studies that gastroliths that made up 1% of the animal's body weight increased lung capacity by 20-40%. It was also found that juvenile American Alligators with gastroliths had their average dive times increased by 88% and maximum dive times increased by 117%. It seems like this is the best explanation out of all the others.

While the increased lung volume seems to be the most credible reason, more research is needed to find the true function of these gastroliths in crocodilians. It is even possible for there to be a combination of reasons for crocodilians to ingest them. It is also worth noting that larger animals seem to ingest more gastroliths in relation to their mass than juveniles. The reason for this is unknown. Only time will tell what the answers to these questions are.

It was believed that gastroliths aided in stability, such as stabilizing crocodilians in the HOTA position shown in this image. However, this doesn't seem to be the case.

Although first believed to help weigh the animal down when underwaer, a more plausible explanation for crocodilians ingesting gastroliths is to help increase dive times. It seems the gastroliths help with expanding the lungs, allowing more air to enter. This would then allow the crocodilian to stay underwater longer.

ACCURATE LIFESPAN

There seems to be no exact number on the lifespan of crocodilians. Compared to other reptiles, crocodilians seem to live much longer, living for several decades, but the lifespan of the animals vary by species and environmental circumstances. It appears based on anecdotal evidence that the smaller species, like most of the caiman species, live shorter lives than the larger species, like the Nile and Saltwater Crocodile. It is also obvious that an animal who is well kept, well fed, and whose health is being monitored constantly is going to live longer than an animal that has to fend for itself in the wild. Many animals from captivity are said to have lived anywhere from 50-100+ years, but are these accounts accurate? Many times the ages of the animals from zoos (especially older animals) are not exact due to the age of the animal being received being not well known. For example, say if an eight foot male American Alligator is dropped off at a zoo. The keepers have no records of the animal's birth, but guess he's 10 years old. From that day onward, the alligator lived for 40 years till its death at the zoo. The animal's age would be guessed at 50 years, but it's just that. A guess, an estimate. What makes this even harder is that the aging process in crocodilians is considerably slower than in mammals. Many crocodilians seem to show very little differences once they've reached sexual maturity versus when they die (some signs of aging do exist though, as will be discussed below).

There are a few ways people have tried to estimate the age of crocodilians. One method is based on size. An average rule thought for most crocodilians is that they grow a foot a year for the first few years of their life, and at a certain point, the growth rate slows down, but continues. By this logic, if one was to see a 15 foot Nile Crocodile, they'd have to assume the animal was old. While it's possible for that to be an old animal, that's not the case every time. Many times, a large crocodilian is not an old one that steadily got bigger, but one that was able to rapidly grow in its earlier years. If the animal after hatching lives in a warm habitat, with little competition, plenty of food, few threats, and has favorable genetics, that animal will be able to grow a lot faster. It is also not true that crocodilians continue to grow noticeably longer their entire life. In terms of their length, eventually they will stop growing or it may slow down to a point where it's barely recognizable. They may continue to grow noticeably in terms of mass though. Another way to determine their age is by counting the growth rings in their osteoderms (bony plates underneath their scutes). Like a tree, the rings show patterns in growth, and by looking at these rings, you'll be able to tell how old the animal is. However, this only works up to a certain point. As the crocodilian gets older and their growth slows down, the spaces in between the rings will get smaller, making it almost impossible to visibly see patterns in growth, thus their age. An alternative way that's being looked into is based on the length of telomeres, or the DNA sequences at the ends of chromosomes. The telomere method is in its early stages however.

While crocodilians do seem to live to old ages, even if the numbers aren't exact, they aren't immortal. While the aging process for crocodilians is slower compared to mammals, it's not as if they don't age. These creatures do naturally age, and they'll succumb to their natural degradation eventually. A couple typical signs of aging in crocodilians are loss of teeth and cataracts. Even with the best care from top tier zoos and veterinarians, they will eventually die. To summarize the lifespan of crocodilians, Gordon Grigg and David Kirshner stated it best, '"they live a long time.'"

Gomek was a large 17.8 ft (5.4 m) Saltwater Crocodile caught in Papua New Guinea in 1968. He lived in captivity for several decades till dying of heart disease in 1997 at the St. Augustine Alligator Farm. According to George Craig, the man who caught Gomek, Gomek looked almost the same when he died as when he was captured. This lack of aging in crocodilians makes it hard to tell how old an animal is.

RAMREE MASSACRE

On February 19th, 1945, towards the end of the Second World War, Japanese Soldiers retreated to the island of Ramree to escape Allied forces. The Japanese moved deeper into the island's swamp to escape, but what waited for them was a fate worse than fighting the opposition. Large Saltwater Crocodiles laid in the depths, grabbing the soldiers one by one and dragging them into the water. Gunshots and screams were heard as the Japanese experienced painful deaths. The water of the swamps rapidly turned red with blood. Vultures feasted on the remains the crocodiles left behind. Of the nearly 1,000 Japanese soldiers that fled into the swamps, only 20 survived. This was "[The] worst crocodile disaster in the world"... supposedly. The truth is there is no evidence to cite this as the worst crocodile attack ever recorded, and there are many problems with this report in general.

One piece of evidence that dismantles the general claim of this incident is the man cited as the main source for the massacre, Bruce Wright, was never actually at Ramree during these attacks. Bruce Wright was a Canadian Naturalist who wrote about many different stories in his book *Wildlife Sketches Near and Far*, and the Ramree Massacre was one of his most famous stories. However, during this time he was at the Ayeyarwady River near Pagan. Therefore, Wright never saw how many Japanese survived, or what conditions these soldiers were dealing with in the first place. One thing that should be noted as well is that he wrote about the incident in the 3rd person, which differs from the rest of his book.

As for those that perished in the swamps of Ramree, they did not die just from crocodiles. Based on military reports, accounts of people who lived on Ramree during the battle, and those who have talked to the Japanese veterans that were there, the reasons for deaths varied. The first danger some soldiers encountered supposedly were sharks as they swam their way to the island's shores. Once the soldiers made it into the swamps, they had to deal with a combination of limited food, dehydration from brackish water, and diseases (especially malaria). These were the main pressures these men faced and the main factors killing them, not crocodiles. While Saltwater Crocodiles did inhabit these swamps and did attack soldiers, the reporting of this was extremely exaggerated. The number of Japanese victims from crocodiles seems to be around 15, nowhere near the number originally reported. It was reported, however, that they did eat the remains of dead soldiers killed by gunfire. In addition, the number of large Saltwater Crocodiles reportedly living in such a dense manner does not make sense. While it is not uncommon for large male Saltwater Crocodiles to coexist in the same waterways, it would seem that there would have been too little resources or space to allow for so many individual crocodiles to live in the Ramree swamps.

While the supposed story of this is fascinating and seems to be perfect for a Hollywood horror film, it is nothing more than a myth. The Guinness World Records, who gave this the title of "Worst crocodile disaster in the world" in 1968, even doubted its legitimacy in its 2017 edition. This myth is as dead as the hundreds lost in this tall tale.

While Allied Soldiers did observe multiple crocodiles eating the remains of dead Japanese soldiers, these soldiers were killed previously by gun fire, not by the crocodiles. The number of Japanese soldiers actually attacked by crocodiles seems to be 15 at most.

REGENERATION

When we think of regeneration in animals, especially reptiles, we commonly think of lizards regrowing their tails. However, it might be hard to imagine that some species of crocodilians have been confirmed to regrow portions of their tails, specifically the tips of their tails. This has been discussed since at least the 20th century, but it is not a well known area of crocodilian biology. There are multiple species across the order Crocodylia that have been described with this ability, but not all have been confirmed to regenerate portions of their tail. It would be reasonable to believe that all have this ability though, as there are multiple representatives in the families Crocodylidae and Alligatoridae, but none have been reported in Gavialidae (at least as of now).

It appears that crocodilians have had this ability to regenerate parts of their tails for some time in their evolutionary history, as revealed by *Steneosaurus bollensis*. It was an aquatic species of crocodylomorph from the Jurassic, which showed early signs of this regeneration. One fossil in particular found a 4.7 inch (12 cm) cartilaginous structure at the end of the 10 foot (3 m) creature's tail. At least in extant species, the regeneration seems to account for 6-18% of the total body length based on recent records, and is mainly seen in adolescent animals with lengths up to 5 ft. Perhaps this is due to younger crocodilians being more likely to be attacked by other animals and a relatively complete tail is more essential for survival. This does not necessarily mean mature individuals lose this ability, but no larger animals with regenerated tails have been documented. The author will note a mature male Tomistoma who's tail tip was bitten off by a mature female Tomistoma at the Los Angeles zoo, and the author observed no signs of regeneration for a period of years after the incident. There was only a stump left where the tail tip was bit off from.

The regenerated portion of the tail is physically distinct from the rest of the tail. The regenerated potion is dark, has an irregular scale pattern, and many times does not resemble the typical flatten/laterally compressed, pointed shape of a normal tail tip. The tail also has no skeletal muscles or a spinal cord, but does have a hollow tube made out of cartilage where a spinal cord would be. The tail is only made up of cartilage and connective tissue. There also seem to be nerves, but only for sensory purposes and not for motor function. This means that the regenerated tail is essentially an non movable paddle for the crocodilian to use in swimming, but it is still useful nonetheless. The tail takes many months to regenerate, with one documented Black Caiman taking up to 18 months to regenerate its tail.

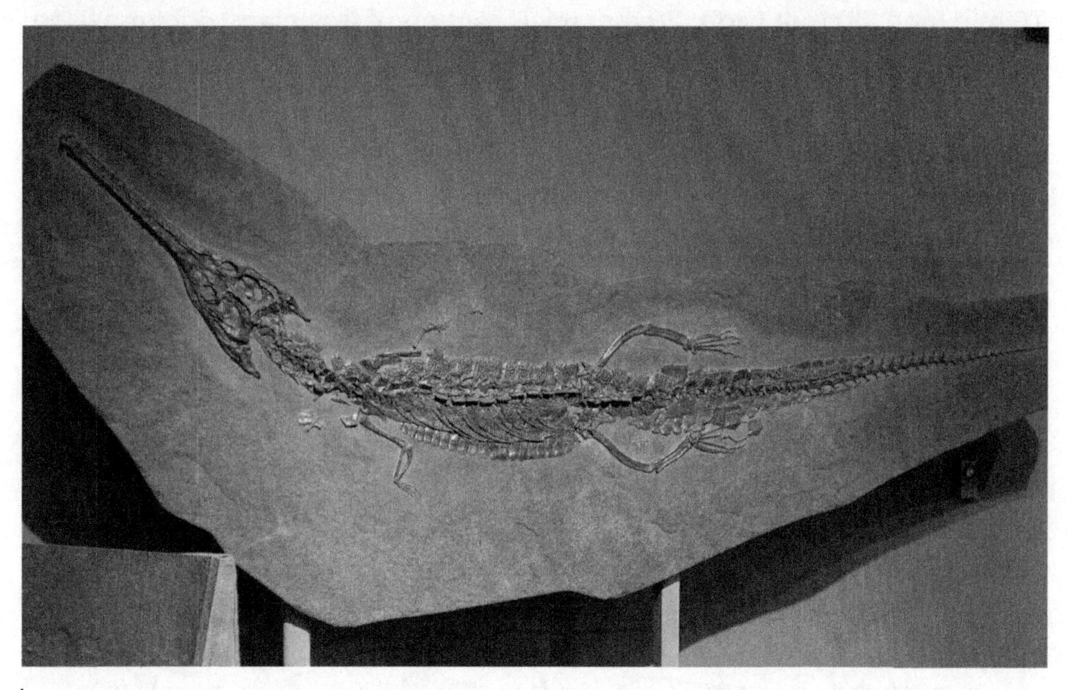

Steneosaurus bollensis *is an extinct crocodylomorph that showed signs of regeneration for its tail.*

This regrown part of the tail is visibly distinct from the rest of the tail. It is only made up of cartilage and connective tissue. The tail also appears somewhat deformed many times, as shown with this regenerated American Alligator tail.

It should be noted that there's the possibility of regeneration beyond tails in crocodilians. An eight year old Mugger Crocodile exhibited partial regeneration of the maxillary bone, or upper jaw, as described by Peter Brazaitis of the New York Zoological Park in the 20th century. A Tomistoma bit the young Mugger and "The resulting injury included the [excision] of a 70 mm long, 40 mm wide, 20 mm thick section of the lateral right maxillary bone [2.8 in x 1.6 in x 0.8 in]." The only treatment that was applied to the injury was nitrofurazone ointment, which is used to prevent bacterial infections. The exposed tooth sockets from the bite naturally sealed and a tooth that was ripped off regenerated with even "greater size" compared to the original. Spongy bone and epidermal tissue was extensively regenerated in 90 days, and the damage seemed to be nearly healed by 45 months. Scar tissue and dark scales were present, much like the tails. Regeneration seems to be an area of crocodilian research that will need further exploration.

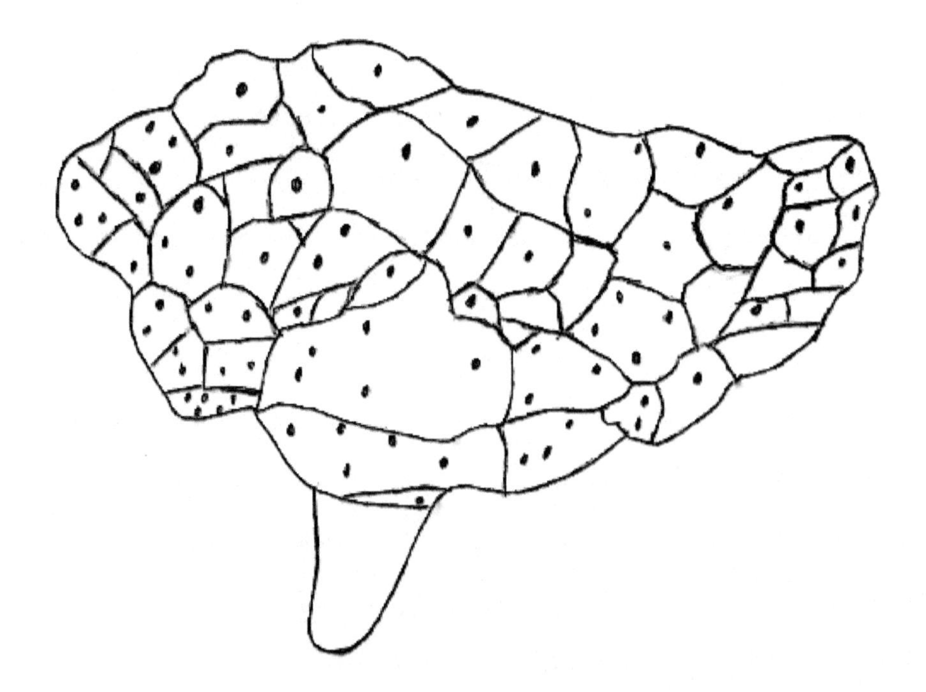

An illustration of the section of jaw of a Mugger Crocodile removed by a Tomistoma.

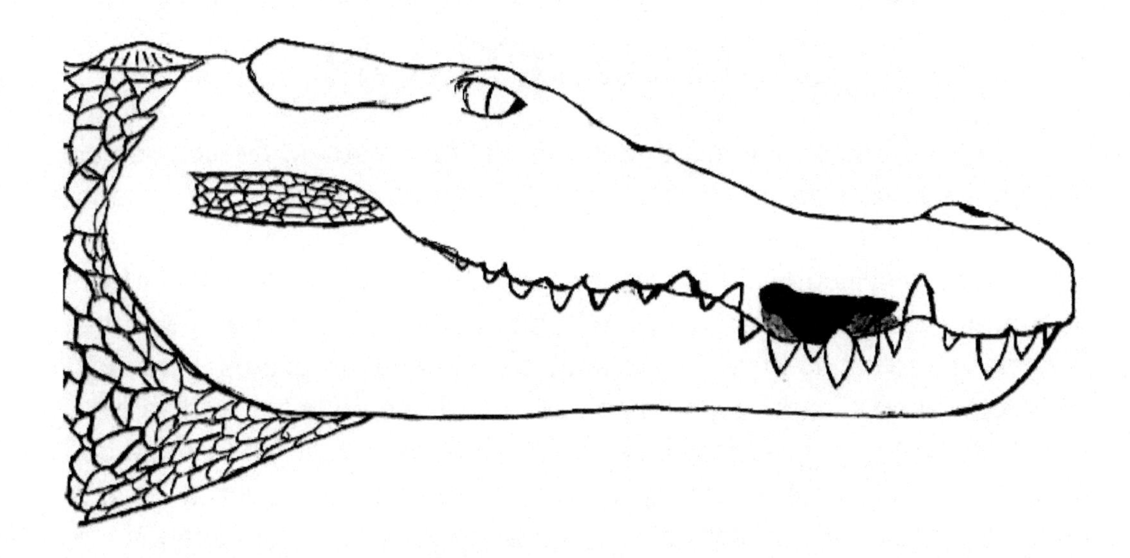

An illustration of the injured Mugger Crocodile after the maxillary bone had healed. The section of the jaw was noticeably different from the rest of the jaw, as it was dark with scar tissue. The tooth that was originally removed not only regenerated, but was larger than the original tooth.

FRUIT AND VEGETABLE CONSUMPTION

For a group of animals that are thought by many to be vicious carnivores, it's surprising to see crocodilians eating their occasional amount of fruits and vegetables. While crocodilians are not considered true omnivores and are still considered carnivores, there are documented incidents of crocodilians eating fruit and vegetable matter. The species that have been observed eating fruits and vegetables vary and this seems to be most commonly seen in captivity, but has been documented in the wild as well.

At the St. Augustine Alligator Farm, keepers have seen American Alligators and Chinese Alligators of the same exhibit going over to a pile of fruits and vegetables for tortoises, and eating tomatoes, romaine lettuce, and yellow squash. In addition, American Alligators have been observed eating kumquats out of the lower parts of a kumquat tree at the same zoo. In many captive settings, crocodilians are also known to investigate their environments and even bite at objects in their enclosures. This includes plants, and sometimes they will even swallow the leaves of trees. In terms of wild observations, some examples include Morelet's Crocodiles and possibly American Crocodiles eating Pond Apples, the Mugger Crocodile eating Cluster Figs, and Siamese Crocodiles eating Watermelons.

The reasons for this behavior are still not certain. Thoughts range from the fruits and vegetables being used as a type of "bio-gastrolith", to consuming them as dietary supplements. There is even debate about whether crocodilians can properly metabolize plant-based nutrients or not. One study even suggested that crocodilians were effective agents for seed dispersal. When looking through the stomachs of various species, many different types of fruit and seeds were found. Considering the fact many crocodilians are known to travel long distances, this is plausible.

This eating behavior was never thought about in detail historically, and was thought just to be accidental. However, after multiple confirmed intentional consumptions of these food items from various species, plus the seed findings, these can not just be random coincidences. Only time will tell why crocodilians have the occasional taste for greens.

A juvenile American Alligator eating yellow squash at the St. Augustine Alligator Farm. This was recorded by the current director of the zoo, John Brueggen, and posted on Youtube. The video is titled "Vegetarian alligators" and it shows a young alligator eating yellow squash from the dishes for the Red-foot Tortoises. The video even shows the same alligator taking away a tomato from the mouth of one tortoise. John Brueggen has previously stated "...it is now a common sight to see the alligators at the tortoise bowls eating romaine lettuce and yellow squash. Sometimes the alligators even beat the tortoises to the dishes."

Zoos commonly give watermelons to crocodilians as enrichment, as the crocodilians like crushing them in their jaws.

BIBLIOGRAPHY

Living Fossils:

Buckland, W., & Buckland, F. T. (1870). In Geology and Mineralogy: As Exhibiting the Power, Wisdom, and Goodness of God Volume 1 (pp. 214–215). Bell and Daldy.
Buckley, G. A., Brochu, C. A., Krause, D. W., & Pol, D. (2000). A Pug-nosed crocodyliform from the late cretaceous of Madagascar. Nature, 405(6789), 941–944. https://doi.org/10.1038/35016061
Brochu, C. A., & Sumrall, C. D. (2020). Modern cryptic species and crocodylian diversity in the fossil record. Zoological Journal of the Linnean Society, 189(2), 700–711. https://doi.org/10.1093/zoolinnean/zlaa039
DK Publishing. (2019). In Smithsonian Dinosaurs and Prehistoric Life: The Definitive Visual Guide to Prehistoric Animals (pp. 198–407).
EastTennesseeState. (2013, January 3). Crocodiles - myth of the living fossils. YouTube. Retrieved February 10, 2022, from https://www.youtube.com/watch?v=T4qzy4kzGnU
Grigg, G. C., & Kirshner, D. (2015). In Biology and Evolution of Crocodylians (pp. 50–74). Comstock Publishing Associates a division of Cornell University Press.
Jabr, F. (2015, March 4). The rise and fall of the living fossil. Nautilus | Science Connected. Retrieved January 16, 2021, from https://nautil.us/the-rise-and-fall-of-the-living-fossil-3041/
Marinho, T. S., & Carvalho, I. S. (2009). An armadillo-like sphagesaurid crocodyliform from the late cretaceous of Brazil. Journal of South American Earth Sciences, 27(1), 36–41. https://doi.org/10.1016/j.jsames.2008.11.005
Melstrom, K. M., & Irmis, R. B. (2019). Repeated evolution of herbivorous crocodyliforms during the age of dinosaurs. Current Biology, 29(14). https://doi.org/10.1016/j.cub.2019.05.076
Schwimmer, D. R. (2002). King of the Crocodylians: The Paleobiology of Deinosuchus. Indiana University Press.
Seymour, R. S., Bennett-Stamper, C. L., Johnston, S. D., Carrier, D. R., & Grigg, G. C. (2004). Evidence for endothermic ancestors of crocodiles at the stem of archosaur evolution. Physiological and Biochemical Zoology, 77(6), 1051–1067. https://doi.org/10.1086/422766
Stevenson, C. (2019). In Crocodiles of the world: A complete Guide to Alligators, Caimans, Crocodiles and Gharials (pp. 14–26). New Holland Publishers.
Willis, P. M. (1997). Review of fossil crocodilians from Australasia. Australian Zoologist, 30(3), 287–298. https://doi.org/10.7882/az.1997.004

The Snout Rule:

Britton, A. (n.d.). Crocodilian species - gharial (Gavialis gangeticus). Retrieved June 4, 2022, from http://crocodilian.com/cnhc/csp_ggan.htm
Caiman crocodilus apaporiensis. Caiman crocodilus subsp. apaporiensis - Plazi TreatmentBank. (n.d.). Retrieved June 4, 2022, from https://tb.plazi.org/GgServer/html/03891D31FFF0FFBCFF6C64A5FAC376F4

crocdoc2. (2017, August 26). How to tell an alligator from a crocodile. YouTube. Retrieved June 1, 2021, from https://www.youtube.com/watch?v=3fdq3-TFT8Y

Erickson, G. M., Gignac, P. M., Steppan, S. J., Lappin, A. K., Vliet, K. A., Brueggen, J. D., Inouye, B. D., Kledzik, D., & Webb, G. J. (2012). Insights into the ecology and evolutionary success of crocodilians revealed through bite-force and tooth-pressure experimentation. PLoS ONE, 7(3). https://doi.org/10.1371/journal.pone.0031781

Grigg, G. C., & Kirshner, D. (2015). In Biology and Evolution of Crocodylians (pp. 88-112). Comstock Publishing Associates a division of Cornell University Press.

Iijima, M., Kubo, T., & Kobayashi, Y. (2018). Comparative limb proportions reveal differential locomotor morphofunctions of alligatoroids and crocodyloids. Royal Society Open Science, 5(3), 171774. https://doi.org/10.1098/rsos.171774

Shaney, K., Shwedick, B., Simpson, B., & Stevenson, C. (n.d.). Tomistoma Tomistoma Schlegelii - iucncsg.org. Retrieved June 5, 2021, from http://www.iucncsg.org/365_docs/attachments/protarea/29250d3a4c25ac44646a45ccf2aeebdc.pdf

St, N. (2018, March 12). A newly discovered difference between alligators and crocodiles. The New York Times. Retrieved August 12, 2019, from https://www.nytimes.com/2018/03/12/science/alligators-crocodiles-differences.html#:~:text=Now%2C%20researchers%20from%20Japan%20have,the%20team%20reported%20last%20week

Stevenson, C. (2019). In Crocodiles of the world: A complete Guide to Alligators, Caimans, Crocodiles and Gharials (pp. 30–263). New Holland Publishers.

Trutnau, L., Sommerlad, R., Haecky, V., Schwarz, D., Nickel, H., & Fuchs, K. (2006). In Crocodilians their natural history & captive husbandry (pp. 143–145). Ed. Chimaira.

Walmsley, C. W., Smits, P. D., Quayle, M. R., McCurry, M. R., Richards, H. S., Oldfield, C. C., Wroe, S., Clausen, P. D., & McHenry, C. R. (2013). Why the long face? the mechanics of mandibular symphysis proportions in crocodiles. PLoS ONE, 8(1). https://doi.org/10.1371/journal.pone.0053873

Crocodile Tears

Britton, A. (n.d.). Crocodilian Biology Database - FAQ - do crocodiles cry "Crocodile tears"? Retrieved September 5, 2020, from https://crocodilian.com/cnhc/cbd-faq-q6.htm#:~:text=The%2016th%20Century%20slaver%20John,surprising%20them%20and%20devouring%20them.

Guggisberg, C. A. W. (1972). In Crocodiles: Their natural history, folklore and conservation (pp. 164–165). Stackpole Books.

Hakluyt, R. (2013). In Principal Navigations Voyages Traffiques and discoveries of the English nation (pp. 40). Cambridge Univ Press.

Martin, G. (n.d.). 'crocodile tears' - the meaning and origin of this phrase. Phrasefinder. Retrieved January 4, 2022, from https://www.phrases.org.uk/meanings/crocodile-tears.html

Moore, C. B. (1954). The Grinning Crocodilian and His Folklore. The Scientific Monthly, 78(4), 225–231.

Morell, V. (2021, May 3). 'crocodile tears' are surprisingly similar to our own. Animals. Retrieved January 4, 2022, from https://www.nationalgeographic.com/animals/article/reptilian-tears

Nath, D. (2021, May 28). Explained: The science and myth behind Crocodile's tears. The Indian Express. Retrieved January 4, 2022, from https://indianexpress.com/article/explained/the-science-and-myth-behind-crocodiles-tears-7333335/

Neill, W. T. (1971). In The last of the ruling reptiles; alligators, crocodiles, and their kin (pp. 16–18). Columbia University Press.

Stevenson, C. (2019). In Crocodiles of the world: A complete Guide to Alligators, Caimans, Crocodiles and Gharials (pp. 89). New Holland Publishers.

Intelligence Level:

Alexander, M. (2006). Last of the Cuban crocodile? with shrinking habitat and threatened by hunting and crossbreeding, this ancient reptile faces possible extinction. The Free Library. Retrieved June 11, 2022, from http://www.thefreelibrary.com/_/print/PrintArticle.aspx?id=141091822

Andy21187. (2021, February 3). Desensitized training with Crocodile. YouTube. Retrieved June 11, 2022, from https://www.youtube.com/watch?v=MFCg8Soyyvg

Andy21187. (2021, January 30). Target training Cuban crocodile. YouTube. Retrieved June 11, 2022, from https://www.youtube.com/watch?v=8bh51Rjd0O4

Dinets, V. (2013). Crocodilians use tools for hunting. Research Gate. Retrieved January 15, 2021, from https://www.researchgate.net/publication/271994159_Crocodilians_use_tools_for_hunting

Grigg, G. C., & Kirshner, D. (2015). In Biology and Evolution of Crocodylians (pp. 161-202). Comstock Publishing Associates a division of Cornell University Press.

NaplesZoo. (2014, May 29). Alligator bay feeding in Naples Zoo at Caribbean Gardens. YouTube. Retrieved June 11, 2022, from https://www.youtube.com/watch?v=nJCk-4Ojqaw

Read, M. A., Grigg, G. C., Irwin, S. R., Shanahan, D., & Franklin, C. E. (2007). Satellite tracking reveals long distance coastal travel and homing by translocated estuarine crocodiles, Crocodylus porosus. PLoS ONE, 2(9). https://doi.org/10.1371/journal.pone.0000949

Stevenson, C. (2019). In Crocodiles of the world: A complete Guide to Alligators, Caimans, Crocodiles and Gharials (pp. 57-59). New Holland Publishers.

Trutnau, L., Sommerlad, R., Haecky, V., Schwarz, D., Nickel, H., & Fuchs, K. (2006). In Crocodilians their natural history & captive husbandry (pp. 148-149). Ed. Chimaira.

Enormous Crocodilians:

Bothwell, D. (1962). In The Great Outdoors Book of Alligators, and other crocodilia (pp. 76–78). Great Outdoors Pub. Co.

Britton, A. (n.d.). Which is the largest species of crocodile? Crocodilian Biology Database - FAQ . Retrieved April 12, 2022, from http://crocodilian.com/cnhc/cbd-faq-q2.htm

Britton, A., Whitaker, N., & Whitaker, R. E. (2012, December). Here be a dragon: Exceptional size in a saltwater crocodile (Crocodylus porosus) from the Philippines . Retrieved April 25, 2021, from https://www.researchgate.net/publication/265511442_Here_be_a_dragon_exceptional_size_in_a_saltwater_crocodile_Crocodylus_porosus_from_the_Philippines

Downes, J. (n.d.). Richard Freeman: Giant crocodiles - the supreme predator. CRYPTOZOOLOGY ONLINE: Still on the Track. Retrieved March 17, 2022, from http://forteanzoology.blogspot.com/2009/03/richard-freeman-giant-crocodiles.html

Evon, D. (2019, November 7). Is this a 28-foot-long crocodile that was killed in Australia in 1957? Snopes.com. Retrieved February 5, 2022, from https://www.snopes.com/fact-check/28-foot-crocodile-killed-australia-1957/

Flower, S. S. (1914). In Report on a zoological mission to India in 1913 (pp. 21–24).

Ministry of Public Works.

Freeman, R. (2022). In search of real monsters adventures in cryptozoology volume 2. MANGO MEDIA.

Garlock, M. (2006). In Killer Gators and crocs: Gruesome encounters from across the globe (pp. 117–119). Globe Pequot Press.

Gibbons, W. (2009, September 20). People ask questions about alligators and William Bartram. Savannah River Ecology Laboratory University of Georgia . Retrieved May 25, 2022, from https://archive-srel.uga.edu/outreach/ecoviews/ecoview090920.htm

Grant, R. (2011). In Crazy river: Exploration and folly in East Africa (pp. 247). Free Press.

Grigg, G. C., & Kirshner, D. (2015). In Biology and Evolution of Crocodylians (pp. 26-30). Comstock Publishing Associates a division of Cornell University Press.

Guggisberg, C. A. W. (1972). In Crocodiles: Their natural history, folklore and conservation (pp. 20-51). Stackpole Books.

Hagenbeck, C., Elliot, H., & Thacker, A. G. (1912). In Beasts and men, being Carl Hagenbeck's experiences for half a century among wild animals (pp. 201–201). Longmans, Green & Co.

Hornaday, W. T. (1914). In The American Natural History; a foundation of useful knowledge of the higher animals of North America (Vol. 4, pp. 10–11). New York Charles Scribner's Sons.

Is Gustave, the monster crocodile of Burundi, still terrorizing the people of Burundi and Tanganyika? is he the largest Nile crocodile ev... Quora. (n.d.). Retrieved June 8, 2022, from https://www.quora.com/Is-Gustave-the-monster-crocodile-of-Burundi-still-terrorizing-the-people-of-Burundi-and-Tanganyika-Is-he-the-largest-Nile-crocodile-ever-recorded

Kingsley, M. H. (1897). Travels in West Africa.

Morgan, G. S., Albury, N. A., Rímoli, R., Lehman, P., Rosenberger, A. L., & Cooke, S. B. (2018). The Cuban crocodile (crocodylus rhombifer) from late quaternary underwater cave deposits in the Dominican Republic. American Museum Novitates, 2018(3916). https://doi.org/10.1206/3916.1

Ouchley, K. (2013). In American Alligator Ancient Predator In The Modern World (pp. 31–33). Univ. Press of Florida.

Pitman, C. R. S. (1925). The length attained by and the habits of the Gharial (G. gangeticus). Journal of the Bombay Natural History Society. 30 (3): 703

Platt, S. G., & Thorbjarnarson, J. B. (2000). Status and conservation of the American crocodile, Crocodylus acutus, in Belize. Biological Conservation, 96(1), 13–20. https://doi.org/10.1016/s0006-3207(00)00038-0

Reese, A. M. (1915). In Alligator and its allies (pp. 2–3). G.P. Putnam's Sons.

Ross, F. D. (n.d.). N Reptilia: Crocodilia: Crocodylidae - Crocodylus rhombifer. Retrieved February 2, 2022, from https://repositories.lib.utexas.edu/bitstream/handle/2152/45471/0680_Crocodylus_rhombifer.pdf?sequence=1

Siege, L. (n.d.). The Monster Crocs of Lake Chamo July 2014, Volume 12-4. African indaba. Retrieved May 5, 2022, from http://www.africanindaba.com/2014/07/the-monster-crocs-of-lake-chamo-july-2014-volume-12-4/

Singh, L.A.K.; Bustard, H.R. (1982). The extinction of the gharial (Gavialis gangeticus (Gmelin)) from the Brahmani and Baitarani Rivers of Orissa. Journal of the Bombay Natural History Society 79(2): 424-425.

Tomistoma. Tomistoma Task Force. (2015, May 3). Retrieved March 3, 2022, from https://tomistomablog.wordpress.com/tomistoma/

Toro, M. A. del. (1974). In Los Crocodylia de Mexico: Estudio comparativo (pp. 14–15). Instituto Mexicano de Recursos Naturales.

Trutnau, L., Sommerlad, R., Haecky, V., Schwarz, D., Nickel, H., & Fuchs, K. (2006). In

Crocodilians their natural history & captive husbandry (pp. 419-585). Ed. Chimaira.
Vigliotti, J. (2020, December 23). 19-foot alligator: The fascinating true story. Grunge.com. Retrieved June 27, 2021, from https://www.grunge.com/127199/19-foot-alligator-the-fascinating-true-story/
What happened to gustave the crocodile? Quora. (n.d.). Retrieved June 8, 2022, from https://www.quora.com/What-happened-to-Gustave-the-crocodile
Which was the biggest crocodile ever found in human history, Gustave or Lolong? Quora. (n.d.). Retrieved June 8, 2022, from https://www.quora.com/Which-was-the-biggest-crocodile-ever-found-in-human-history-Gustave-or-Lolong
Whitaker, R. & Basu, D. (1982). The Gharial (Gavialis gangeticus): A review. Journal of the Bombay Natural History Society. 79 (3): 531–548.
Whitaker, R., & Whitaker, N. (n.d.). Who's got the biggest? - iucncsg.orgR. Retrieved April 25, 2021, from https://www.iucncsg.org/365_docs/attachments/protarea/907d4ded022a4ddefe525f89ee64b150.pdf
World's largest reptile found in India - ohmynews international. (n.d.). Retrieved March 28, 2022, from https://web.archive.org/web/20080108203350/http://english.ohmynews.com/articleview/article_view.asp?no=298369&rel_no=1

Trochilus/Plover and Other Symbiotic Relationships

Britton, A. (2009, September 6). Crocodile myths #1 - the curious trochilus. Blog Spot. Retrieved October 13, 2019, from http://crocodilian.blogspot.com/2009/09/crocodile-myths-1-curious-trochilus.html
Carl, N. J., Stewart, H. A., & Paul, J. S. (2020). Unprovoked mouth gaping behavior in extant Crocodylia. Journal of Herpetology, 54(4). https://doi.org/10.1670/18-157
Cott, H.B. (1961): Scientific results of an inquiry into the ecology and economic status of the Nile Crocodile (Crocodylus niloticus) in Uganda and Northern Rhodesia. Trans. Zool. Soc. London 29: 211-356
Coughlin, S. (2020, October 25). Providential ecology in Herodotus and Aristotle. Ancient Medicine. Retrieved February 5, 2022, from https://www.ancientmedicine.org/home/2018/12/18/providential-ecology-in-herodotus-and-aristotle
Crocodile with Egyptian plover. Warren Photographic. (n.d.). Retrieved October 12, 2019, from https://www.warrenphotographic.co.uk/01080-crocodile-with-egyptian-plover
de la Rosa, C. L. (2014). Additional observations of lachryphagous butterflies and bees. Frontiers in Ecology and the Environment, 12(4), 210–210. https://doi.org/10.1890/14.wb.006
Guggisberg, C. A. W. (1972). In Crocodiles: Their natural history, folklore and conservation (pp. 75-79). Stackpole Books.
Herodotus and Lynn Margulis: Conversation. Lapham's Quarterly. (n.d.). Retrieved June 8, 2022, from https://www.laphamsquarterly.org/conversations/herodotus-lynn-margulis
Mesiluk. (n.d.). Apple Valley, Minnesota. West African dwarf crocodile, osteolaemus tetraspis getting the inside of his mouth cleaned by cleaner fish which removes and eats parasites and other materials. 123RF. Retrieved April 15, 2022, from https://www.123rf.com/photo_169239814_apple-valley-minnesota-west-african-dwarf-crocodile-osteolaemus-tetraspis-getting-the-inside-of-his-.html?vti=n9y1flnalx9ecnned5-1-12
Nile crocodile with Egyptian plover photograph, WP00955. Warren Photographic. (n.d.). Retrieved October 12, 2019, from https://www.warrenphotographic.co.uk/00955-nile-crocodile-with-egyptian-plover

packypacka. (2007, December 14). Dentyne white - crocodile bird. YouTube. Retrieved June 8, 2022, from https://www.youtube.com/watch?v=UIDdCihh5hU
Poole, D. F. (1961). Notes on tooth replacement in the nile crocodile, crocodylus niloticus. Proceedings of the Zoological Society of London, 136(1), 131–140. https://doi.org/10.1111/j.1469-7998.1961.tb06083.x
Reilly, L. (2019, February 25). 13 bizarre descriptions of the ancient world according to herodotus's histories. Mental Floss. Retrieved February 2, 2022, from https://www.mentalfloss.com/article/571789/herodotus-histories
Tellez, M., & Merchant, M. (2015). Biomonitoring heavy metal pollution using an aquatic apex predator, the American alligator, and its parasites. PLOS ONE, 10(11). https://doi.org/10.1371/journal.pone.0142522
Trutnau, L., Sommerlad, R., Haecky, V., Schwarz, D., Nickel, H., & Fuchs, K. (2006). In Crocodilians their natural history & captive husbandry (pp. 233). Ed. Chimaira.
Wu, P., Wu, X., Jiang, T.-X., Elsey, R. M., Temple, B. L., Divers, S. J., Glenn, T. C., Yuan, K., Chen, M.-H., Widelitz, R. B., & Chuong, C.-M. (2013). Specialized stem cell niche enables repetitive renewal of alligator teeth. Proceedings of the National Academy of Sciences, 110(22). https://doi.org/10.1073/pnas.1213202110
Wylie, D. (2013). In Crocodile (pp. 12–13). Reaktion Books. Retrieved February 17, 2022, from https://books.apple.com/us/book/crocodile/id1091051317?ign-mpt=uo%3D4.

Running Speeds:

Bharti, B. (2019, December 17). Crocodiles can gallop now? yes, but don't worry, alligators can't. National Post. Retrieved December 17, 2019, from https://nationalpost.com/news/world/crocodiles-alligators-caiman-gallop-leap-bound
Britton, A. (n.d.). How fast can a crocodile run? Crocodilian Biology Database - FAQ. Retrieved December 10, 2019, from https://crocodilian.com/cnhc/cbd-faq-q4.htm
Grigg, G. C., & Kirshner, D. (2015). In Biology and Evolution of Crocodylians (pp. 137-142). Comstock Publishing Associates a division of Cornell University Press.
Hutchinson, J. R., Felkler, D., Houston, K., Chang, Y.-M., Brueggen, J., Kledzik, D., & Vliet, K. A. (2019). Divergent evolution of terrestrial locomotor abilities in extant Crocodylia. Scientific Reports, 9(1). https://doi.org/10.1038/s41598-019-55768-6
Iijima, M., Kubo, T., & Kobayashi, Y. (2018). Comparative limb proportions reveal differential locomotor morphofunctions of alligatoroids and crocodyloids. Royal Society Open Science, 5(3), 171774. https://doi.org/10.1098/rsos.171774
Renous, S., Gasc, J. P., Bels, V. L., & Wicker, R. (2002). Asymmetrical gaits of juvenile crocodylus johnstoni, galloping Australian crocodiles. Journal of Zoology, 256(3), 311–325.
Stevenson, C. (2019). In Crocodiles of the world: A complete Guide to Alligators, Caimans, Crocodiles and Gharials (pp. 84). New Holland Publishers.
St, N. (2018, March 12). A newly discovered difference between alligators and crocodiles. The New York Times. Retrieved June 5, 2022, from https://www.nytimes.com/2018/03/12/science/alligators-crocodiles-differences.html#:~:text=Now%2C%20researchers%20from%20Japan%20have,the%20team%20reported%20last%20week.
Webb, G. J., & Gans, C. (1982). Galloping in crocodylus johnstoni—a reflection of terrestrial activity? Records of the Australian Museum, 34(14), 607–618. https://doi.org/10.3853/j.0067-1975.34.1982.244

Alligators Living In New York Sewers:

Alderson, D. (2020). In America's alligator: A popular history of our most celebrated reptile (pp. 87–89). Lyons Press.
Alligator in the sewer day 2020. Google Sites: Sign-in. (n.d.). Retrieved April 12, 2022, from https://sites.google.com/view/sewer-alligator-evidence/home
Alligator in the sewer day 2020 - Nyt sewer gator story. Google Sites: Sign-in. (n.d.). Retrieved April 11, 2022, from https://sites.google.com/view/sewer-alligator-evidence/nyt-sewer-gator-story?authuser=0
Daley, R. (n.d.). The World Beneath the City. The world beneath the city, Robert Daley, 1959. Retrieved February 2, 2022, from https://www.sewergator.com/lit/world_beneath_the_city.htm
Figura, D. (2017, August 7). Watch: 2nd alligator captured in Upstate Ny River (video). newyorkupstate. Retrieved March 5, 2022, from https://www.newyorkupstate.com/southern-tier/2017/08/watch_2nd_alligator_captured_in_upstate_ny_river_video.html
Gannett Satellite Information Network. (2019, July 16). Elusive alligator 'chance the snapper' finally caught by Florida expert in Chicago lagoon. USA Today. Retrieved March 10, 2022, from https://www.usatoday.com/story/news/2019/07/16/chicago-alligator-chance-snapper-captured-expert-police-say/1742482001/
Garlock, M. (2006). In Killer Gators and crocs: Gruesome encounters from across the globe (pp. 57-59). Globe Pequot Press.
Guardian News and Media. (2007, May 25). Reggie the alligator captured from La Lake. The Guardian. Retrieved March 3, 2022, from https://www.theguardian.com/world/2007/may/25/usa
Helsel, P. (2010, August 23). Gator crawls out of Queens drain. New York Post. Retrieved March 3, 2020, from https://nypost.com/2010/08/23/gator-crawls-out-of-queens-drain/
Huynh, N. (2017, July 26). Alligator loose in upstate ny: Kayakers who spotted it couldn't believe their eyes. syracuse. Retrieved March 5, 2020, from https://www.syracuse.com/state/2017/07/kayakers_spotted_alligator_on_loose_in_upstate_ny_village.html
Itzkowitz, L., Lambert, A., Madrigal, I., Rose, B., Sheidlower, N., & Untapped New York. (2021, August 30). Could there be alligators in NYC's sewer? Untapped New York. Retrieved December 1, 2021, from https://untappedcities.com/2021/07/06/alligators-in-nyc-sewer/
Kilgannon, C. (2020, February 26). The truth about alligators in the sewers of New York. The New York Times. Retrieved March 10, 2020, from https://www.nytimes.com/2020/02/26/nyregion/alligators-sewers-new-york.html
Krystek, L. (n.d.). Allegations of Alligators in the Sewers of New York. The UNMUSEUM. Retrieved January 15, 2021, from http://www.unmuseum.org/sgator.htm
Mikkelson, D. (1999, July 10). Can alligators live in sewers? Snopes.com. Retrieved September 10, 2019, from https://www.snopes.com/fact-check/alligators-sewers/
New Jersey Sewergator: July 21, 1907. (n.d.). Retrieved September 12, 2019, from https://www.sewergator.com/news/nyt19070721.htm
Postal workers find live alligator chewing through shipping carton. Journal Times. (2003, November 16). Retrieved June 5, 2021, from https://journaltimes.com/news/state-and-regional/postal-workers-find-live-alligator-chewing-through-shipping-carton/article_638e1d47-1848-5bed-98d0-3b0e2b72831d.html
Sewergators in the news. (n.d.). Retrieved March 5, 2022, from https://www.sewergator.com/news/news.htm
UPI. (2001, June 23). The Future of NYC Reptile Uncertain. UPI. Retrieved October 3, 2019, from https://www.upi.com/Archives/2001/06/23/The-future-of-NYC-reptile-uncertain/2227993268800/

Working Sewergator: March 2, 1915. (n.d.). Retrieved March 4, 2022, from https://www.sewergator.com/news/eo19150302.htm

Current Taxonomy:

Balaguera-Reina, S. A. (2019). Rediscovering the Apaporis Caiman (caiman crocodilus apaporiensis): Notes from a long-anticipated expedition. Journal of Herpetology, 53(4), 310. https://doi.org/10.1670/19-028

Borges, V. S., Santiago, P. C., Lima, N. G., Coutinho, M. E., Eterovick, P. C., & Carvalho, D. C. (2018). Evolutionary significant units within populations of neotropical broad-snouted caimans (caiman latirostris, Daudin, 1802). Journal of Herpetology, 52(3), 282–288. https://doi.org/10.1670/17-074

Britton, A. (n.d.). Tomistoma (Tomistoma Schlegelii). Crocodilian species. Retrieved May 15, 2022, from https://crocodilian.com/cnhc/csp_tsch.htm

Brochu, C. A., & Sumrall, C. D. (2020). Modern cryptic species and crocodylian diversity in the fossil record. Zoological Journal of the Linnean Society, 189(2), 700–711. https://doi.org/10.1093/zoolinnean/zlaa039

Crocodilian species. iucncsg.org. (n.d.). Retrieved September 20, 2019, from http://www.iucncsg.org/pages/Crocodilian-Species.html

Eaton, J. E. J. (n.d.). Dwarf crocodile crocodile osteolaemus tetraspis - iucncsg. org. IUCNCSG. Retrieved May 17, 2022, from https://www.iucncsg.org/365_docs/attachments/protarea/21%20O-c1d8ab26.pdf

Endo, H., Aoki, R., Taru, H., Kimura, J., Sasaki, M., Yamamoto, M., Arishima, K., & Hayashi, Y. (2002). Comparative functional morphology of the masticatory apparatus in the long-snouted crocodiles. Anatomia, Histologia, Embryologia: Journal of Veterinary Medicine Series C, 31(4), 206–213. https://doi.org/10.1046/j.1439-0264.2002.00396.x Godshalk, R. (2014). Rivers, mountains, deserts: the fractured Neotropics – how many caimans are there? 23rd Working Meeting of the IUCN Crocodile Specialist Group. IUCN, 348–361.

Grigg, G. C., & Kirshner, D. (2015). In Biology and Evolution of Crocodylians (pp. 5-50). Comstock Publishing Associates a division of Cornell University Press.

Harshman, J., Huddleston, C. J., Bollback, J. P., Parsons, T. J., & Braun, M. J. (2003). True and false gharials: A nuclear gene phylogeny of Crocodylia. Systematic Biology, 52(3), 386–402. https://doi.org/10.1080/10635150390197028

Kaur, T., Japning, J. R., Sabki, M. S., Sidik, I., Chong, L. K., & Ong, A. H. (2013). Genetic diversity of tomistoma schlegelii inferred from mtdna markers. Biochemical Genetics, 51(3-4), 275–295. https://doi.org/10.1007/s10528-012-9562-9

Medem, F. (1955). A new subspecies of Caiman sclerops from Colombia. https://doi.org/10.5962/bhl.title.3168

Merchant, M., Hale, A., Brueggen, J., Harbsmeier, C., & Adams, C. (2018). Crocodiles alter skin color in response to environmental color conditions. Scientific Reports, 8(1). https://doi.org/10.1038/s41598-018-24579-6

Merchant, M. E., Mills, K., Leger, N., Jerkins, E., Vliet, K. A., & McDaniel, N. (2006). Comparisons of innate immune activity of all known living crocodylian species. Comparative biochemistry and physiology. Part B, Biochemistry & molecular biology, 143(2), 133–137. https://doi.org/10.1016/j.cbpb.2005.10.005

Murray, C. M., Russo, P., Zorrilla, A., & McMahan, C. D. (2019). Divergent morphology among populations of the New Guinea crocodile, Crocodylus Novaeguineae (Schmidt, 1928): Diagnosis of an independent lineage and description of a new species. Copeia, 107(3), 517. https://doi.org/10.1643/cg-19-240

Oaks, J. R. (2011). A time-calibrated species tree of Crocodylia reveals a recent radiation of the true crocodiles. Evolution, 65(11), 3285–3297. https://doi.org/10.1111/j.1558-5646.2011.01373.x

O'Shea, M. (n.d.). CROCODYLIA: CROCODILES & ALLIGATORS. Mark O'Shea - the official website. Retrieved June 9, 2022, from https://www.markoshea.info/photography_crocodylia.php

Piras, P., Colangelo, P., Adams, D. C., Buscalioni, A., Cubo, J., Kotsakis, T., Meloro, C., & Raia, P. (2010). The Gavialis-Tomistoma debate: The contribution of skull ontogenetic allometry and growth trajectories to the study of Crocodylian Relationships. Evolution & Development, 12(6), 568–579. https://doi.org/10.1111/j.1525-142x.2010.00442.x Rio, J. P., & Mannion, P. D. (2021). Phylogenetic analysis of a new morphological dataset elucidates the evolutionary history of Crocodylia and resolves the long-standing gharial problem. PeerJ, 9. https://doi.org/10.7717/peerj.12094

Schwimmer, D. R. (2002). In King of the Crocodylians: The paleobiology of deinosuchus (pp. 158–159). Indiana University Press.

Shaney, K., Shwedick, B., Simpson, B., & Stevenson, C. (n.d.). Tomistoma Tomistoma Schlegelii - iucncsg.org. IUCNCSG. Retrieved January 5, 2021, from http://www.iucncsg.org/365_docs/attachments/protarea/29250d3a4c25ac44646a45ccf2aeebdc.pdf

Shirley, M. H., Carr, A. N., Nestler, J. H., Vliet, K. A., & Brochu, C. A. (2018). Systematic revision of the living African slender-snouted crocodiles (mecistops gray, 1844). Zootaxa, 4504(2), 151. https://doi.org/10.11646/zootaxa.4504.2.1

Species accounts. iucncsg.org. (n.d.). Retrieved January 1, 2021, from http://www.iucncsg.org/pages/Species-Accounts.html

Stevenson, C. (2019). Crocodiles of the world: A complete guide to alligators, Caimans, crocodiles and gharials. New Holland Publishers.

Tarsitano, S. F., Frey, E., & Riess, J. (1989). The evolution of the Crocodilia: A conflict between morphological and biochemical data. American Zoologist, 29(3), 843–856. https://doi.org/10.1093/icb/29.3.843

Trutnau, L., Sommerlad, R., Haecky, V., Schwarz, D., Nickel, H., & Fuchs, K. (2006). In Crocodilians their natural history & captive husbandry (pp. 530-32). Ed. Chimaira.

Yirka, B. (2018, January 31). Strange orange cave dwelling african dwarf crocodiles could be evolving into a new species. Phys.org. Retrieved September 15, 2019, from https://phys.org/news/2018-01-strange-orange-cave-african-dwarf.html

Yong, E. (2011, September 14). Nile crocodile is two species. Nature News. Retrieved June 10, 2022, from https://www.nature.com/articles/news.2011.535

True Use of Gastroliths:

Darby, D. G., & Ojakangas, R. W. (1980). Gastroliths from an Upper Cretaceous Plesiosaur. Journal of Paleontology, 54(3), 548–556. http://www.jstor.org/stable/1304197

Grigg, G. C., & Kirshner, D. (2015). In Biology and Evolution of Crocodylians (pp. 157-161). Comstock Publishing Associates a division of Cornell University Press.

Henderson, D. M. (2003). Effects of stomach stones on the buoyancy and equilibrium of a floating crocodilian: A computational analysis. Canadian Journal of Zoology, 81(8), 1346–1357. https://doi.org/10.1139/z03-122

Manafzadeh, A. R. (2019, January 1). Why do crocs eat rocks? Integrative Organismal Biology. Retrieved March 3, 2021, from https://iobopen.com/2019/01/02/why-do-crocs-eat-rocks/

Myth or fact: crocodiles eat stones to affect their buoyancy. Life Science Presentations and Labs by Mary Vogas. (2015, September 2). Retrieved September 15, 2019, from http://maryvogas.com/blog/myth-or-fact-crocodiles-eat-stones-to-affect-their-buoyancy

Stevenson, C. (n.d.). Paleosuchus Ecology. Crocodilian.com. Retrieved June 20, 2022, from http://crocodilian.com/paleosuchus/ecology.html

Trutnau, L., Sommerlad, R., Haecky, V., Schwarz, D., Nickel, H., & Fuchs, K. (2006). In Crocodilians their natural history & captive husbandry (pp. 151). Ed. Chimaira.

Wedel, M. (2007, May). Gastroliths. Retrieved December 15, 2019, from https://ucmp.berkeley.edu/taxa/verts/archosaurs/gastroliths.php

Wylie, D. (2013). In Crocodile (pp. 17). Reaktion Books. Retrieved February 17, 2022, from https://books.apple.com/us/book/crocodile/id1091051317?ign-mpt=uo%3D4.

Accurate Lifespan:

Britton, A. (n.d.). Which is the largest species of crocodile? Crocodilian Biology Database - FAQ . Retrieved April 12, 2022, from http://crocodilian.com/cnhc/cbd-faq-q2.htm

Britton, A., Whitaker, N., & Whitaker, R. E. (2012, December). Here be a dragon: Exceptional size in a saltwater crocodile (Crocodylus porosus) from the Philippines . Retrieved April 25, 2021, from https://www.researchgate.net/publication/265511442_Here_be_a_dragon_exceptional_size_in_a_saltwater_crocodile_Crocodylus_porosus_from_the_Philippines

Grigg, G. C., & Kirshner, D. (2015). In Biology and Evolution of Crocodylians (pp. 37-38). Comstock Publishing Associates a division of Cornell University Press.

Moscato, D. (2019, September 25). No, crocodiles are not immortal. Earth Touch News Network. Retrieved October 1, 2019, from https://www.earthtouchnews.com/natural-world/natural-world/no-crocodiles-are-not-immortal/

Scott, N. M., Haussmann, M. F., Elsey, R. M., Trosclair, P. L., & Vleck, C. M. (2006). Telomere length shortens with body length in alligator mississippiensis. Southeastern Naturalist, 5(4), 685–692. https://doi.org/10.1656/1528-7092(2006)5[685:tlswbl]2.0.co;2

Trutnau, L., Sommerlad, R., Haecky, V., Schwarz, D., Nickel, H., & Fuchs, K. (2006). In Crocodilians their natural history & captive husbandry (pp. 152-156). Ed. Chimaira.

Tucker, A. D. (1997). Validation of skeletochronology to determine age of freshwater crocodiles (crocodylus johnstoni). Marine and Freshwater Research, 48(4), 343. https://doi.org/10.1071/mf96113

Xu, M., Wu, X.-B., Yan, P., & Zhu, H.-tao. (2009). Telomere length shortens with age in Chinese alligators (alligator sinensis). Journal of Applied Animal Research, 36(1), 109–112. https://doi.org/10.1080/09712119.2009.9707042

Ramree Massacre:

DeLong, W. (2021, November 19). "A cacophony of hell": The deadliest crocodile attack on humans in recorded history. All That's Interesting. Retrieved June 10, 2022, from https://allthatsinteresting.com/ramree-island

Grigg, G. C., & Kirshner, D. (2015). In Biology and evolution of crocodylians (pp. 612–613). Comstock Publishing Associates a division of Cornell University Press.

Grundhauser, E. (2016, February 27). When crocodiles attack: The Ramree Island Massacre. Atlas Obscura. Retrieved October 12, 2019, from https://www.atlasobscura.

com/articles/the-ramree-island-massacre
natgeoUK. (2016, December 8). Guinness World record of worst crocodile disaster | nazi weird war two | national geographic UK. YouTube. Retrieved June 10, 2022, from https://www.youtube.com/watch?v=00kBr0uxlYA
Platt, S. G., Myo Myo, W. K. K. K., Lay Lay Khaing, L. L., & Rainwater, T. R. (n.d.). MAN EATING BY ESTUARINE CROCODILES: THE RAMREE ISLAND MASSACRE REVISITED. British Herpetological Society. Retrieved October 12, 2019, from https://www.thebhs.org/publications/the-herpetological-bulletin/issue-number-75-spring-2001
Swatman, R. (2016, December 13). National Geographic Channel and Guinness World Records investigate Crocodile Attack Record. Guinness World Records. Retrieved October 15, 2019, from https://www.guinnessworldrecords.com/news/2016/12/national-geographic-channel-and-guinness-world-records-investigate-crocodile-atta-455138
Teng, J. (2021, May 9). Saltwater crocodiles devoured 500 Japanese soldiers in burma during World War 2. Medium. Retrieved April 4, 2022, from https://historyofyesterday.com/saltwater-crocodiles-devoured-500-japanese-soldiers-in-burma-during-world-war-2-3225172aaffe
Wikimedia Foundation. (2022, June 6). Battle of Ramree Island. Wikipedia. Retrieved October 12, 2019, from https://en.wikipedia.org/wiki/Battle_of_Ramree_Island#cite_note-FOOTNOTERussell1987216Kynaston1998135-1

Regeneration:

Brazaitis, P. (1981). Maxillary regeneration in a marsh crocodile, Crocodylus palustris. Journal of Herpetology, 15(3), 360. https://doi.org/10.2307/1563441
Campbell, G. R., & Winterbotham, A. L. (1985). In Jaws too: The natural history of crocodilians with emphasis on Sanibel Island's alligators (pp. 116–117). Sutherland Pub.
Eshanahan. (2020, August 25). Tail regeneration in macrospondylus bollensis or "Steneosaurus". Sobek's Swimming Pool. Retrieved June 5, 2022, from https://sobekswimmingpool.wordpress.com/2020/08/25/tail-regeneration-in-macrospondylus-bollensis-or-steneosaurus/
Magazine, S. (2020, December 28). Alligators are now the largest species known to regrow severed limbs. Smithsonian.com. Retrieved June 5, 2022, from https://www.smithsonianmag.com/smart-news/alligators-are-now-largest-species-known-regrow-severed-limbs-180976628/#:~:text=Gators%20can%20reach%2015%20feet,reports%20Marika%20Gerken%20for%20CNN
Mailonline, I. R. F. (2020, November 24). Regeneration: Alligators can regrow their tails by up to 9 inches after they have been bitten off. Daily Mail Online. Retrieved June 5, 2022, from https://www.dailymail.co.uk/sciencetech/article-8981537/Regeneration-Alligators-REGROW-tails-9-inches-bitten-off.html
Neill, W. T. (1971). In The last of the ruling reptiles; alligators, crocodiles, and their kin (pp. 6). Columbia University Press.
Roth, A. (2021, May 3). Alligators can regrow severed tails, surprising scientists. Animals. Retrieved June 5, 2022, from https://www.nationalgeographic.com/animals/article/alligators-can-regrow-their-tails
Rumford, J. (n.d.). Teleosaurid size estimation: Tables. Palaeontologia Electronica Volume 22, Issue 3 September-December 2019. Retrieved June 5, 2022, from https://palaeo-electronica.org/content/2016/358-648/1571-teleosaurid-size-estimation-tables

Xu, C., Palade, J., Fisher, R. E., Smith, C. I., Clark, A. R., Sampson, S., Bourgeois, R., Rawls, A., Elsey, R. M., Wilson-Rawls, J., & Kusumi, K. (2020). Anatomical and histological analyses reveal that tail repair is coupled with regrowth in wild-caught, Juvenile American alligators (alligator mississippiensis). Scientific Reports, 10(1). https://doi.org/10.1038/s41598-020-77052-8

Fruit and Vegetable Consumption:

Brito, S. P., Andrade, D. V., & Abe, A. S. (2002). Do caimans eat fruit? Retrieved June 12, 2022, from http://www1.rc.unesp.br/ib/zoologia/denis/reprints%20-%20pdf/Frugivory.pdf

Brueggen, J. (2002.). Crocodilians eating their vegetables. St. Augustine Alligator Farm Zoological Park. Retrieved May 18, 2022, from https://www.alligatorfarm.com/blog-item/crocodilians-eating-their-vegetables/

Grigg, G. C., & Kirshner, D. (2015). In Biology and Evolution of Crocodylians (pp. 218–219). Comstock Publishing Associates a division of Cornell University Press.

Platt, S. G., Elsey, R. M., Liu, H., Rainwater, T. R., Nifong, J. C., Rosenblatt, A. E., Heithaus, M. R., & Mazzotti, F. J. (2013). Frugivory and seed dispersal by crocodilians: An overlooked form of Saurochory? Journal of Zoology, 291(2), 87–99. https://doi.org/10.1111/jzo.12052

Schultz, C. (2013, August 23). Kumquat-eating crocodilians: Crocs and Gators love their fruits and Veggies. Smithsonian.com. Retrieved June 5, 2022, from https://www.smithsonianmag.com/smart-news/kumquat-eating-crocodilians-crocs-and-gators-love-their-fruits-and-veggies-1372378/

Stevenson, C. (2019). In Crocodiles of the world: A complete Guide to Alligators, Caimans, Crocodiles and Gharials (pp. 89-90). New Holland Publishers.

Trutnau, L., Sommerlad, R., Haecky, V., Schwarz, D., Nickel, H., & Fuchs, K. (2006). In Crocodilians their natural history & captive husbandry (pp. 149–213). Ed. Chimaira.

Zooguy2. (2007, May 18). Vegetarian alligators. YouTube. Retrieved May 18, 2022, from https://www.youtube.com/watch?v=hUssz3ykeOo

Zooguy2. (2008, August 17). Alligator eating kumquats. YouTube. Retrieved May 18, 2022, from https://www.youtube.com/watch?v=Urdn2m__PQI

IMAGE CREDITS

Covers & Preface:

American Alligator: Sterling Lanier/Unsplash.com
Crocodile Scales: David Clode/unsplash (desaturated)
Spectacled Caiman: Gaetano Cessati/unsplash.com

Living Fossils:

Terrestrisuchus: Nobu Tamura (http://spinops.blogspot.com), CC BY-SA 3.0 <http://creativecommons.org/licenses/by-sa/3.0/>, via Wikimedia Commons
Dakosaurus: Creator: Dmitry Bogdanov, CC BY 3.0 <https://creativecommons.org/licenses/by/3.0>, via Wikimedia Commons
Simosuchus: Smokeybjb, CC BY-SA 3.0 <https://creativecommons.org/licenses/by-sa/3.0>, via Wikimedia Commons
Armadillosuchus: Nobu Tamura (http://spinops.blogspot.com), CC BY-SA 3.0 <https://creativecommons.org/licenses/by-sa/3.0>, via Wikimedia Commons
Isisfordia: Smokeybjb, CC BY-SA 3.0 <https://creativecommons.org/licenses/by-sa/3.0>, via Wikimedia Commons
Boverisuchus: DagdaMor, CC BY-SA 4.0 <https://creativecommons.org/licenses/by-sa/4.0>, via Wikimedia Commons
Mourasuchus: Cidade et al., 2017, CC BY-SA 4.0 <https://creativecommons.org/licenses/by-sa/4.0>, via Wikimedia Commons
Mekosuchus: Manuel Mújica
Wiliam Buckland: Kelson, Public domain, via Wikimedia Commons

The Snout Rule:

Hatchling Saltwater Crocodile: Dwiputras/123rf.com https://www.123rf.com/profile_dwiputras
Saltwater Crocodile: User:AngMoKio, CC BY-SA 2.5 <https://creativecommons.org/licenses/by-sa/2.5>, via Wikimedia Commons

Large Saltwater Crocodile: Michael/Unsplash.com
American Alligator: Shelly Collins/Unsplash.com
Mugger Crocodile: Lakshmi Narasimha/Unsplash.com
Dwarf Crocodile: Staycoolandbegood, Public domain, via Wikimedia Commons
Morelet's Crocodile: Punithsureshgowda, CC BY-SA 3.0 <https://creativecommons.org/licenses/by-sa/3.0>, via Wikimedia Commons (Cropped)
Siamese Crocodile: Luckythanya/Shutterstock.com
American Crocodile: Prince Patel/Unsplash.com
Spectacled Caiman: Ryan Chin/Shutterstock.com
Smooth-fronted Caiman: Artur Bogacki/Shutterstock.com
Broad-snouted Caiman: Walter S. Prado, CC BY-SA 4.0 <https://creativecommons.org/licenses/by-sa/4.0>, via Wikimedia Commons
Tomistoma: TimVickers, Public domain, via Wikimedia Commons
Indian Gharial: Charles J. Sharp, CC BY-SA 4.0 <https://creativecommons.org/licenses/by-sa/4.0>, via Wikimedia Commons

Crocodile Tears:

Grant Illustration: Bernhard Gillam, Public domain, via Wikimedia Commons

Intelligence Level:

Naples Zoo Feeding: Tim Menzies, CC BY-SA 2.0 <https://creativecommons.org/licenses/by-sa/2.0>, via Wikimedia Commons
Los Angeles Zoo Tomistoma: Jake Miller (author)
Cuban Crocodiles: Skansen Aquarium, CC0, via Wikimedia Commons
Saltwater Crocodile: Thomas Quine, CC BY 2.0 <https://creativecommons.org/licenses/by/2.0>, via Wikimedia Commons

Enormous Crocodilians:

American Alligator: Lisa Yount/Unsplash.com
Black Caiman: Renting C/ Unsplash.com
American Crocodile: Bradley Feller/Unsplash.com
Cuban Crocodile: NasserHalaweh, CC BY-SA 4.0 <https://creativecom-

mons.org/licenses/by-sa/4.0>, via Wikimedia Commons
Orinoco Crocodile: slowmotiongli/shutterstock
Nile Crocodile: Jeremy Bezanger https://unsplash.com/photos/aMD-2pL2zyY8 via Unsplash
Saltwater Crocodile: Bernard DUPONT from FRANCE, CC BY-SA 2.0 <https://creativecommons.org/licenses/by-sa/2.0>, via Wikimedia Commons
Tomistoma: Ilham.nurwansah, CC BY-SA 4.0 <https://creativecommons.org/licenses/by-sa/4.0>, via Wikimedia Commons
Indian Gharial: Charles J. Sharp, CC BY-SA 4.0 <https://creativecommons.org/licenses/by-sa/4.0>, via Wikimedia Commons
Crocodile Skull: Everglades NPS from Homestead, Florida, United States, Public domain, via Wikimedia Commons
Lolong in water: MartyWilliams, CC BY-SA 3.0 <https://creativecommons.org/licenses/by-sa/3.0>, via Wikimedia Commons
Lolong preserved: Julan Shirwod Nueva, CC BY-SA 4.0 <https://creativecommons.org/licenses/by-sa/4.0>, via Wikimedia Commons (Cropped)
Lolong Skeleton: Julan Shirwod Nueva, CC BY-SA 4.0 <https://creativecommons.org/licenses/by-sa/4.0>, via Wikimedia Commons (Cropped)

Trochilus/Plover and Other Symbiotic Relationships:

Illustration of Crocodile & Trochilus: Henry Scherren, Public domain, via Wikimedia Commons
Digital Recreation of Relationship:Juniors Bildarchiv GmbH / Alamy Stock Photo
Butterflies Drinking Crocodile Tears: Bernard DUPONT, CC BY-SA 2.0 <https://creativecommons.org/licenses/by-sa/2.0>, via Wikimedia Commons
Dwarf Crocodile With Fish: Mesiluk/124rf.com https://www.123rf.com/profile_mesiluk

Running Speeds:

Nile Crocodile: Leon Pauleikhoff/Unsplash.com
Freshwater Crocodile: [1], CC BY 2.0 <https://creativecommons.org/li-

censes/by/2.0>, via Wikimedia Commons

Alligators Living In New York Sewers:

Albino Alligator: The original uploader was HawkeyeLonewolf at English Wikipedia., CC BY 2.5 <https://creativecommons.org/licenses/by/2.5>, via Wikimedia Commons

Alligator Movie Poster: Moviestore Collection/Alamy Stock Photo

Hatchling Alligators: Abigail Lawson. Public domain., Public domain, via Wikimedia Commons

Reggie the Alligator: Junkyardsparkle, CC0, via Wikimedia Commons

Current Taxonomy:

Nile Crocodile: Bernard Gagnon, CC BY-SA 3.0 <https://creativecommons.org/licenses/by-sa/3.0>, via Wikimedia Commons

West African Crocodile: Atamari, CC BY-SA 3.0 <https://creativecommons.org/licenses/by-sa/3.0>, via Wikimedia Commons

West African Slender-snouted Crocodile: Destination8infinity, CC BY-SA 3.0 <https://creativecommons.org/licenses/by-sa/3.0>, via Wikimedia Commons

Central African Slender-snouted Crocodile: Tim Strater from Rotterdam, Nederland, CC BY-SA 2.0 <https://creativecommons.org/licenses/by-sa/2.0>, via Wikimedia Commons

Central African Dwarf Crocodile: Olivier Testa, CC BY-SA 3.0 <https://creativecommons.org/licenses/by-sa/3.0>, via Wikimedia Commons

Congo Dwarf Crocodile: Marius Burger, CC0, via Wikimedia Commons

West African Dwarf Crocodile: Francesco Veronesi, CC BY-SA 2.0 <https://creativecommons.org/licenses/by-sa/2.0>, via Wikimedia Commons

New Guinea Crocodile: Wilfried Berns www.Tierdoku.com, CC BY-SA 2.0 DE <https://creativecommons.org/licenses/by-sa/2.0/de/deed.en>, via Wikimedia Commons

Hall's New Guinea Crocodile: Midori, CC BY 3.0 <https://creativecommons.org/licenses/by/3.0>, via Wikimedia Commons

Tomistoma: Haplochromis, CC by 2.5 <https://creativecommons.org/licenses/by-sa/2.5/deed.en, via Wikimedia Commons

Indian Gharial: Matěj Baťha, CC BY-SA 3.0 <https://creativecommons.org/licenses/by-sa/3.0>, via Wikimedia Commons
Thoracosaur skull:Ghedoghedo, CC BY-SA 3.0 <https://creativecommons.org/licenses/by-sa/3.0>, via Wikimedia Commons
Rio Apaporis Caiman Head Illustration : Manuel Mújica

True Use of Gastroliths:

Gastroliths: Wilson44691, CC BY-SA 3.0 <https://creativecommons.org/licenses/by-sa/3.0>, via Wikimedia Commons
Crocodile Feeding: Deva Darshan/Unsplash.com
HOTA Position: Giedriius/123rf.com https://www.123rf.com/profile_giedriius
Crocodile Underwater: Alexander Machulskiy/Shutterstock.com

Accurate Lifespan:

Gomek: Mattmayhugh, Public domain, Via Wikipedia

Ramree Massacre:

Saltwater Crocodiles: shellac, CC BY 2.0 <https://creativecommons.org/licenses/by/2.0>, via Wikimedia Commons

Regeneration:

Steneosaurus: Greg Goebel from Loveland CO, USA, CC BY-SA 2.0 <https://creativecommons.org/licenses/by-sa/2.0>, via Wikimedia Commons
Regenerated Tail: (pg.)Xu, C., Palade, J., Fisher, R. E., Smith, C. I., Clark, A. R., Sampson, S., Bourgeois, R., Rawls, A., Elsey, R. M., Wilson-Rawls, J., & Kusumi, K. (2020). Anatomical and histological analyses reveal that tail repair is coupled with regrowth in wild-caught, Juvenile American alligators (alligator mississippiensis). Scientific Reports, 10(1). https://doi.org/10.1038/s41598-020-77052-8
Removed Section of Jaw Illustration: Jake Miller (author)

Regenerated Jaw Illustration: Jake Miller (author)

Fruit and Vegetable Consumption:

Alligator Eating Yellow Squash: John Brueggen, Zooguy2. (2007, May 18). Vegetarian alligators. YouTube. Retrieved May 18, 2022, from https://www.youtube.com/watch?v=hUssz3ykeOo

Crocodile with Watermelon: dpa picture alliance/Alamy Stock Photo

Printed in Great Britain
by Amazon

25328144R00046